# Applied Engineering: Studies of God's Design in Nature

## MASTER BOOKS
### — CURRICULUM —

First printing: March 2014
Ninth printing: February 2020

Master Books®, P.O. Box 726, Green Forest, AR 72638
Master Books® is a division of the New Leaf Publishing Group, Inc.

ISBN: 978-0-89051-989-9
ISBN: 978-1-61458-063-8 (digital)

**Printed in the United States of America**

Please visit our website for other great titles:
www.masterbooks.com

For information regarding author interviews,
please contact the publicity department at (870) 438-5288

**Master Books Creative Team:**
**Editor:** Craig Froman
**Design:** Terry White
**Copy Editors:**
Judy Lewis, Willow Meek
**Curriculum Review:**
Kristen Pratt
Laura Welch
Diana Bogardus

**Author Bios:**

**Jeff Seto** has worked as an aerospace engineer in experimental research and development for over 20 years; holds a B. Eng in aerospace and an electrical engineering diploma in avionics.

**Ray Comfort** is a best-selling author of more than 70 books, and the president of Living Waters ministry.

**Dr. Henry Morris** is known as the father of modern Creation science, the founder of Institute for Creation Research (ICR) and the author of many well-known apologetic books.

**Don DeYoung** is Chairman of the Science and Mathematics Department, Grace College, Winona Lake, Indiana.

**Derrik Hobbs** has an active interest in creation studies, including business models based on principles and processes found in nature.

Your reputation as a publisher is stellar. It is a blessing knowing anything I purchase from you is going to be worth every penny!

—Cheri ★ ★ ★ ★ ★

Last year we found Master Books and it has made a HUGE difference.

—Melanie ★ ★ ★ ★ ★

We love Master Books and the way it's set up for easy planning!

—Melissa ★ ★ ★ ★ ★

You have done a great job. MASTER BOOKS ROCKS!

—Stephanie ★ ★ ★ ★ ★

Physically high-quality, Biblically faithful, and well-written.

—Danika ★ ★ ★ ★ ★

Best books ever. Their illustrations are captivating and content amazing!

—Kathy ★ ★ ★ ★ ★

## Affordable
## Flexible
## Faith Building

## Table of Contents

**Features:** The suggested weekly schedule enclosed has easy-to-manage lessons that guide the reading, worksheets, and all assessments. The pages of this guide are perforated and three-hole punched so materials are easy to tear out, hand out, grade, and store. Teachers are encouraged to adjust the schedule and materials needed in order to best work within their unique educational program.

**Lesson Scheduling:** Students are instructed to read the pages in their book and then complete the corresponding section provided by the teacher. Assessments that may include worksheets, activities, quizzes, and tests are given at regular intervals with space to record each grade. Space is provided on the weekly schedule for assignment dates, and flexibility in scheduling is encouraged. Teachers may adapt the scheduled days per each unique student situation. As the student completes each assignment, this can be marked with an "X" in the box.

| | |
|---|---|
| | Approximately 30 to 45 minutes per lesson, four days a week |
| | Includes answer keys for worksheets, quizzes, and tests |
| | Worksheets for each section |
| | Quizzes and tests are included to help reinforce learning and provide assessment opportunities. |
| | Designed for grades 7 to 9 in a one-year course to earn 1 science credit |
| | Applied Learning Activities |

**Course Objectives:** Students completing this course will

✓ Evaluate how things like batteries, human organ repair, microlenses, automotive engineering, paint, and even credit card security all have links to natural designs

✓ Review how design in nature reveals the fingerprint of our Creator

✓ Discover how the glow of a cat's eyes innovates road reflectors

✓ Investigate the naturally sticky inspirations for Velcro® and barbed wire, as well as how a fly's

ear, the lizard's foot, the moth's eye, and other natural examples are inspiring improvements and new technologies in our lives

✓ Study the life of the "forgotten" inventor, Joseph Henry, whose exploration of electricity set the standard for later innovators

✓ Identify how the exploration of practical intelligent design in nature offers a new paradigm for science inquiry.

# Course Description

This *Applied Engineering: Studies of God's Design in Nature* teacher guide contains materials for use with *Made in Heaven, Men of Science, Men of God*, and *Discovery of Design*. From the frontiers of scientific discovery, researchers are now taking design elements from the natural world and creating extraordinary breakthroughs that benefit our health, our quality of life, and our ability to communicate, and even help us work more efficiently. An exciting look at cutting-edge scientific advances, the course highlights incredible examples that include innovations like solar panels in space unfurled using technology gleaned from beech tree leaves, and optic research rooted in the photonic properties of opal gemstones.

Science continually borrows from God's creation, yet refuses to give God the glory. Engineers and inventors have long examined God's creation to understand and copy complex, proven mechanics of design in the science known as biomimicry. Much of this inspiration is increasingly drawn from amazing aspects of nature in search of wisdom and insight. We are surrounded daily by scientific advancements that have become everyday items, simply because man is copying from God's incredible creation.

There is nothing in science that can ever prove that God does not exist and therefore, no way that science can disprove the possibility of miracles or of true creation. Science cannot either prove or disprove such things, and so a scientist can decide for himself whether he will believe them. The observed facts and data of science can support him in this choice or otherwise, but they can never compel it. It is completely wrong for people to assume — as they often do — that a true scientist cannot simultaneously be a true man of God, believing in God as Creator and Savior and believing the Bible as God's revelation.

Note: Answers to the Digging Deeper portions of the worksheets can be found in the back of the *Discovery of Design* text used for this course.

# Research Paper

Before the end of this course, a student is required to write a research paper on an inventor from *Men of Science, Men of God*. In the book, Dr. Henry Morris presents 101 biographies which include Christian testimonies of scientists who believed in the Bible and in a personal Creator God . . . scientists who were pioneers and "founding fathers" of modern scientific disciplines. One can begin reading the book and exploring the inventors in anticipation of this paper.

# First Semester Suggested Daily Schedule

| Date | Day | Assignment | Due Date | ✓ | Grade |
|------|-----|------------|----------|---|-------|
| | | First Semester–First Quarter | | | |
| Week 1 | Day 1 | Introduction & Ch 1: Microorganisms: Bacteria-Micro-motor<br>Read Pages 8–13, 188 (the appropriate answer section)<br>*Discovery of Design* • (DoD)<br>*Discovery of Design*: Intro & Worksheet 1 • Pages 16–17<br>Teacher Guide • (TG) | | | |
| | Day 2 | Ch 1: Bacteria-Battery • Read Pages 14–15, 189 • (DoD)<br>*Discovery of Design*: Worksheet 2 • Page 18 • (TG) | | | |
| | Day 3 | Ch 1: Biofilm-Bacteria Control • Read Pages 16–17, 189 • (DoD)<br>*Discovery of Design*: Worksheet 3 • Page 19 • (TG) | | | |
| | Day 4 | Ch 1: Diatom-Nanotechnology • Read Pages 18–19, 190 • (DoD)<br>*Discovery of Design*: Worksheet 4 • Page 20 • (TG) | | | |
| | Day 5 | | | | |
| Week 2 | Day 6 | Ch 1: Protien-Solar Cells • Read Pages 20–21, 190 • (DoD)<br>*Discovery of Design*: Worksheet 5 • Page 21 • (TG) | | | |
| | Day 7 | Ch 2: The Insect World: Ants-Airlines<br>Read Pages 23–25, 191 • (DoD)<br>*Discovery of Design*: Intro & Worksheet 1 • Pages 22–23 • (TG) | | | |
| | Day 8 | Ch 2: Asian Beetle-Paper Whitener<br>Read Pages 26–27, 191 • (DoD)<br>*Discovery of Design*: Worksheet 2 • Page 24 • (TG) | | | |
| | Day 9 | | | | |
| | Day 10 | | | | |
| Week 3 | Day 11 | Ch 2: Bombardier Beetle-Gas Turbine Engine<br>Read Pages 28–29, 191 • (DoD)<br>*Discovery of Design*: Worksheet 3 • Page 25 • (TG) | | | |
| | Day 12 | Ch 2: Butterfly-Cosmetics • Read Pages 30–31, 192 • (DoD)<br>*Discovery of Design*: Worksheet 4 • Page 26 • (TG) | | | |
| | Day 13 | Ch 2: Dragonfly-Surveillance • Read Pages 32–33, 192 • (DoD)<br>*Discovery of Design*: Worksheet 5 • Page 27 • (TG) | | | |
| | Day 14 | Ch 2: Firefly-Light Stick • Read Pages 34–35, 193 • (DoD)<br>*Discovery of Design*: Worksheet 6 • Page 28 • (TG) | | | |
| | Day 15 | | | | |
| Week 4 | Day 16 | Ch 2: Fly-Hearing Aid • Read Pages 36–37, 193 • (DoD)<br>*Discovery of Design*: Worksheet 7 • Page 29 • (TG) | | | |
| | Day 17 | Ch 2: Honey Bee-Surveillance • Read Pages 38–39, 194 • (DoD)<br>*Discovery of Design*: Worksheet 8 • Page 30 • (TG) | | | |
| | Day 18 | Ch 2: Insect Hearing-Atomic Force Microscope<br>Read Pages 40–41, 194 • (DoD)<br>*Discovery of Design*: Worksheet 9 • Page 31 • (TG) | | | |
| | Day 19 | Ch 2: Insects-Robotics • Read Pages 42–43, 195 • (DoD)<br>*Discovery of Design*: Worksheet 10 • Page 32 • (TG) | | | |
| | Day 20 | | | | |

| Date | Day | Assignment | Due Date | ✓ | Grade |
|------|-----|-----------|----------|---|-------|
| **Week 5** | Day 21 | Ch 2: Namib Beetle-Water Collector<br>Read Pages 44–45, 195 • (DoD)<br>*Discovery of Design*: Worksheet 11 • Page 33 • (TG) | | | |
| | Day 22 | Ch 2: Spider Silk-Fiber Optics • Read Pages 46–47, 196 • (DoD)<br>*Discovery of Design*: Worksheet 12 • Page 34 • (TG) | | | |
| | Day 23 | Ch 2: Termite Mound-Ventilation<br>Read Pages 48–49, 196 • (DoD)<br>*Discovery of Design*: Worksheet 13 • Page 35 • (TG) | | | |
| | Day 24 | Ch 2: Timber Beetle Larva • Read Pages 50–51, 196 • (DoD)<br>*Discovery of Design*: Worksheet 14 • Page 36 • (TG) | | | |
| | Day 25 | | | | |
| **Week 6** | Day 26 | Ch 2: Wasp-Paper • Read Pages 52–53, 197 • (DoD)<br>*Discovery of Design*: Worksheet 15 • Page 37 • (TG) | | | |
| | Day 27 | Ch 2: Water Strider-Water Repellent<br>Read Pages 54–55, 197 • (DoD)<br>*Discovery of Design*: Worksheet 16 • Page 38 • (TG) | | | |
| | Day 28 | ***Discovery of Design*: Ch.1–2 Quiz 1** • Pages 191–192 • (TG) | | | |
| | Day 29 | Ch 3: Flight: Bat-Sonar Systems<br>Read Pages 57–59, 198 • (DoD)<br>*Discovery of Design*: Worksheet 1 • Page 39 • (TG) | | | |
| | Day 30 | | | | |
| **Week 7** | Day 31 | Ch 3: Bird Flight-Aircraft • Read Pages 60–61, 198 • (DoD)<br>*Discovery of Design*: Worksheet 2 • Page 40 • (TG) | | | |
| | Day 32 | Ch 3: Flying Reptile-Delta Wing Aircraft<br>Read Pages 62–63, 199 • (DoD)<br>*Discovery of Design*: Worksheet 3 • Page 41 • (TG) | | | |
| | Day 33 | Ch 3: Kingfisher-Bullet Train • Read Pages 64–65, 199 • (DoD)<br>*Discovery of Design*: Worksheet 4 • Page 42 • (TG) | | | |
| | Day 34 | Ch 3: Owl Wing-Noise Reduction<br>Read Pages 66–67, 200 • (DoD)<br>*Discovery of Design*: Worksheet 5 • Page 43 • (TG) | | | |
| | Day 35 | | | | |
| **Week 8** | Day 36 | Ch 3: Swift-Aircraft Wings • Read Pages 68–69, 200 • (DoD)<br>*Discovery of Design*: Worksheet 6 • Page 44 • (TG) | | | |
| | Day 37 | Ch 3: Toucan Beak-Shock Absorber<br>Read Pages 70–71, 201 • (DoD)<br>*Discovery of Design*: Worksheet 7 • Page 45 • (TG) | | | |
| | Day 38 | Ch 4: Underwater Life: Boxfish-Automobile Design<br>Read Pages 73–75, 201 • (DoD)<br>*Discovery of Design*: Worksheet 1 • Page 47 • (TG) | | | |
| | Day 39 | Ch 4: Brittlestar-Microlens • Read Pages 76–77, 202 • (DoD)<br>*Discovery of Design*: Worksheet 2 • Page 48 • (TG) | | | |
| | Day 40 | | | | |

| Date | Day | Assignment | Due Date | ✓ | Grade |
|---|---|---|---|---|---|
| **Week 9** | Day 41 | Ch 4: Cuttlefish-Camouflage • Read Pages 78–79, 202 • (DoD)<br>*Discovery of Design*: Worksheet 3 • Page 49 • (TG) | | | |
| | Day 42 | Ch 4: Elephant Nose Fish-Electric Sensor<br>Read Pages 80–81, 203 • (DoD)<br>*Discovery of Design*: Worksheet 4 • Page 50 • (TG) | | | |
| | Day 43 | Ch 4: Fish Motion-Ship Propulsion<br>Read Pages 82–83, 203 • (DoD)<br>*Discovery of Design*: Worksheet 5 • Page 51 • (TG) | | | |
| | Day 44 | Ch 4: Lobster Eye-Telescope Lens<br>Read Pages 84–85, 204 • (DoD)<br>*Discovery of Design*: Worksheet 6 • Page 52 • (TG) | | | |
| | Day 45 | | | | |
| First Semester–Second Quarter | | | | | |
| **Week 1** | Day 46 | Ch 4: Mussels-Adhesive • Read Pages 86–87, 204 • (DoD)<br>*Discovery of Design*: Worksheet 7 • Page 53 • (TG) | | | |
| | Day 47 | Ch 4: Octopus-Robotics • Read Pages 88–89, 205 • (DoD)<br>*Discovery of Design*: Worksheet 8 • Page 54 • (TG) | | | |
| | Day 48 | Ch 4: Seashell-Construction Material<br>Read Pages 90–91, 205 • (DoD)<br>*Discovery of Design*: Worksheet 9 • Page 55 • (TG) | | | |
| | Day 49 | Ch 4: Sea Slug-Chemicals • Read Pages 92–93, 206 • (DoD)<br>*Discovery of Design*: Worksheet 10 • Page 56 • (TG) | | | |
| | Day 50 | | | | |
| **Week 2** | Day 51 | Ch 4: Sea Sponge-Fiber Optics-Chemicals<br>Read Pages 94–95, 206 • (DoD)<br>*Discovery of Design*: Worksheet 11 • Page 57 • (TG) | | | |
| | Day 52 | Ch 4: Whale-Submarine • Read Pages 96–97, 206 • (DoD)<br>*Discovery of Design*: Worksheet 12 • Page 58 • (TG) | | | |
| | Day 53 | *Discovery of Design*: **Ch. 3–4 Quiz 2** • Pages 195–198 • (TG) | | | |
| | Day 54 | Ch 5: Land Animals: Ankylosaurus-Fiberglass<br>Read Pages 99–101, 207 • (DoD)<br>*Discovery of Design*: Worksheet 1 • Page 59 • (TG) | | | |
| | Day 55 | | | | |
| **Week 3** | Day 56 | Ch 5: Antler-Organ Repair • Read Pages 102–103, 207 • (DoD)<br>*Discovery of Design*: Worksheet 2 • Page 60 • (TG) | | | |
| | Day 57 | Ch 5: Dog Paw-Shoe Soles • Read Pages 104–105, 208 • (DoD)<br>*Discovery of Design*: Worksheet 3 • Page 61 • (TG) | | | |
| | Day 58 | Ch 5: Gecko-Adhesive • Read Pages 106–107, 208 • (DoD)<br>*Discovery of Design*: Worksheet 4 • Page 62 • (TG) | | | |
| | Day 59 | Ch 5: Giraffe-Antigravity Spacesuit<br>Read Pages 108–109, 208 • (DoD)<br>*Discovery of Design*: Worksheet 5 • Page 63 • (TG) | | | |
| | Day 60 | | | | |

| Date | Day | Assignment | Due Date | ✓ | Grade |
|---|---|---|---|---|---|
| **Week 4** | Day 61 | Ch 5: Horse Bone-Construction<br>Read Pages 110–111, 209 • (DoD)<br>*Discovery of Design*: Worksheet 6 • Page 64 • (TG) | | | |
| | Day 62 | Ch 5: Penguin Eye-Sunglasses<br>Read Pages 112–113, 209 • (DoD)<br>*Discovery of Design*: Worksheet 7 • Page 65 • (TG) | | | |
| | Day 63 | Ch 5: Tree Frog-Automobile Tires<br>Read Pages 114–115, 210 • (DoD)<br>*Discovery of Design*: Worksheet 8 • Page 66 • (TG) | | | |
| | Day 64 | Ch 6: People: Body Odor-Insect Repellent<br>Read Pages 117–119, 210 • (DoD)<br>*Discovery of Design*: Worksheet 1 • Page 67 • (TG) | | | |
| | Day 65 | | | | |
| **Week 5** | Day 66 | Ch 6: DNA-Computer Memory<br>Read Pages 120–121, 210 • (DoD)<br>*Discovery of Design*: Worksheet 2 • Page 68 • (TG) | | | |
| | Day 67 | Ch 6: DNA-Eardrum-Earphone<br>Read Pages 122–123, 211 • (DoD)<br>*Discovery of Design*: Worksheet 3 • Page 69 • (TG) | | | |
| | Day 68 | Ch 6: Eye Iris-Identification • Read Pages 124–125, 211 • (DoD)<br>*Discovery of Design*: Worksheet 4 • Page 70 • (TG) | | | |
| | Day 69 | Ch 6: Fibrin-Elastic • Read Pages 126–127, 212 • (DoD)<br>*Discovery of Design*: Worksheet 5 • Page 71 • (TG) | | | |
| | Day 70 | | | | |
| **Week 6** | Day 71 | Ch 6: Fingerprint-Prosthetic Hand<br>Read Pages 128–129, 212 • (DoD)<br>*Discovery of Design*: Worksheet 6 • Page 72 • (TG) | | | |
| | Day 72 | Ch 6: Leg Bone-Eiffel Tower • Read Pages 130–131, 213 • (DoD)<br>*Discovery of Design*: Worksheet 7 • Page 73 • (TG) | | | |
| | Day 73 | Ch 6: Muscles-Robotics • Read Pages 132–133, 213 • (DoD)<br>*Discovery of Design*: Worksheet 8 • Page 74 • (TG) | | | |
| | Day 74 | Ch 6: Saliva-Healing • Read Pages 134–135, 214 • (DoD)<br>*Discovery of Design*: Worksheet 9 • Page 75 • (TG) | | | |
| | Day 75 | | | | |
| **Week 7** | Day 76 | Ch 6: Skin-Self-repairing Plastic<br>Read Pages 136–137, 214 • (DoD)<br>*Discovery of Design*: Worksheet 10 • Page 76 • (TG) | | | |
| | Day 77 | Ch 6: Tooth Enamel-Armor Coating<br>Read Pages 138-139, 214 • (DoD)<br>*Discovery of Design*: Worksheet 11 • Page 77 • (TG) | | | |
| | Day 78 | Ch 6: Vernix-Skin Cream • Read Pages 140-141, 215 • (DoD)<br>*Discovery of Design*: Worksheet 12 • Page 78 • (TG) | | | |
| | Day 79 | *Discovery of Design*: **Ch. 5–6 Quiz 3** • Pages 199–202 • (TG) | | | |
| | Day 80 | | | | |

| Date | Day | Assignment | Due Date | ✓ | Grade |
|------|-----|------------|----------|---|-------|
| **Week 8** | Day 81 | Ch 7: Vegetation: Beech Leaf-Space Antenna<br>Read Pages 143–145, 215 • (DoD)<br>*Discovery of Design*: Worksheet 1 • Page 79 • (TG) | | | |
| | Day 82 | Ch 7: Chemicals-Medicine • Read Pages 146–149, 216 • (DoD)<br>*Discovery of Design*: Worksheet 2 • Page 80 • (TG) | | | |
| | Day 83 | Ch 7: Cocklebur-Velcro • Read Pages 150–151, 216 • (DoD)<br>*Discovery of Design*: Worksheet 3 • Page 81 • (TG) | | | |
| | Day 84 | Ch 7: Fava Bean-Valve • Read Pages 152–153, 217 • (DoD)<br>*Discovery of Design*: Worksheet 4 • Page 82 • (TG) | | | |
| | Day 85 | | | | |
| **Week 9** | Day 86 | Ch 7: Fescue Grass-Herbicide<br>Read Pages 154–155, 217 • (DoD)<br>*Discovery of Design*: Worksheet 5 • Page 83 • (TG) | | | |
| | Day 87 | Ch 7: Lotus Flower-Surface Cleaner<br>Read Pages 156–157, 217 • (DoD)<br>*Discovery of Design*: Worksheet 6 • Page 84 • (TG) | | | |
| | Day 88 | Ch 7: Osage Orange-Barbed Wire<br>Read Pages 158–159, 218 • (DoD)<br>*Discovery of Design*: Worksheet 7 • Page 85 • (TG) | | | |
| | Day 89 | Ch 7: Pine Cone-Smart Clothes<br>Read Pages 160–161, 218 • (DoD)<br>*Discovery of Design*: Worksheet 8 • Page 86 • (TG) | | | |
| | Day 90 | | | | |
| | | Mid-Term Grade | | | |

| Date | Day | Assignment | Due Date | ✓ | Grade |
|------|-----|------------|----------|---|-------|
| | | Second Semester–Third Quarter | | | |
| **Week 1** | Day 91 | Ch 7: Rubber Tree-Automobile Tires<br>Read Pages 162–163, 219 • (DoD)<br>*Discovery of Design*: Worksheet 9 • Page 87 • (TG) | | | |
| | Day 92 | Ch 7: Skunk Cabbage-Thermostat<br>Read Pages 164–165, 219 • (DoD)<br>*Discovery of Design*: Worksheet 10 • Page 88 • (TG) | | | |
| | Day 93 | Ch 7: Spinach-Solar Cell • Read Pages 166–167, 220 • (DoD)<br>*Discovery of Design*: Worksheet 11 • Page 89 • (TG) | | | |
| | Day 94 | Ch 7: Venus Flytrap-Food Packaging<br>Read Pages 168–169, 220 • (DoD)<br>*Discovery of Design*: Worksheet 12 • Page 90 • (TG)) | | | |
| | Day 95 | | | | |
| **Week 2** | Day 96 | Ch 7: Water Lily-Construction • Read Pages 170–171, 221 • (DoD)<br>*Discovery of Design*: Worksheet 13 • Page 91 • (TG) | | | |
| | Day 97 | Ch 7: Wild Wheat-Humidity Sensor<br>Read Pages 172–173, 221 • (DoD)<br>*Discovery of Design*: Worksheet 14 • Page 92 • (TG) | | | |
| | Day 98 | Ch 8: Nonliving Objects: Buckyballs-Micro Ball Bearings<br>Read Pages 175–177, 221 • (DoD)<br>*Discovery of Design*: Worksheet 1 • Page 93 • (TG) | | | |
| | Day 99 | Ch 8: Nanoparticles-Water Purifier<br>Read Pages 178–179, 222 • (DoD)<br>*Discovery of Design*: Worksheet 2 • Page 94 • (TG) | | | |
| | Day 100 | | | | |
| **Week 3** | Day 101 | Ch 8: Opal-Photonic Device<br>Read Pages 180–181, 222 • (DoD)<br>*Discovery of Design*: Worksheet 3 • Page 95 • (TG) | | | |
| | Day 102 | Ch 8: Pulsar-Time Standard • Read Pages 182–183, 223 • (DoD)<br>*Discovery of Design*: Worksheet 4 • Page 96 • (TG) | | | |
| | Day 103 | Ch 8: Water Flow-Impeller & Conclusion<br>Read Pages 184–187, 223 • (DoD)<br>*Discovery of Design*: Worksheet 5 • Page 97 • (TG) | | | |
| | Day 104 | ***Discovery of Design*: Ch. 7–8 Quiz 4** • Pages 203–206 • (TG) | | | |
| | Day 105 | | | | |
| **Week 4** | Day 106 | ***Discovery of Design*: Ch. 1–8 Test** • Pages 207–210 • (TG) | | | |
| | Day 107 | Forward & Intro • Read Pages 1–7 • *Made in Heaven* • (MiH)<br>*Made in Heaven*: Worksheet 1 • Page 101 • (TG) | | | |
| | Day 108 | Ch 1: Swim Like a Fish • Read Pages 8–9 • (MiH)<br>*Made in Heaven*: Worksheet 1 • Page 103–104 • (TG) | | | |
| | Day 109 | Introduction: • Read Pages 5–10 • *Men of Science, Men of God*<br>• (MOS) | | | |
| | Day 110 | | | | |

| Date | Day | Assignment | Due Date | ✓ | Grade |
|------|-----|------------|----------|---|-------|
| **Week 5** | Day 111 | Ch 1: Swim Like a Fish<br>*Made in Heaven*: Worksheet 2 • Pages 105–106 • (TG) | | | |
| | Day 112 | Ch 2: Body Armor of the Future • Read Pages 10-11 • (MiH)<br>*Made in Heaven*: Worksheet 1 • Pages 107–108 • (TG) | | | |
| | Day 113 | Ch 3: Stronger than Kevlar • Read Pages 12-13 • (MiH)<br>*Made in Heaven*: Worksheet 1 • Pages 109–110 • (TG) | | | |
| | Day 114 | Ch 1: • Read Pages 11–13 • (MOS) | | | |
| | Day 115 | | | | |
| **Week 6** | Day 116 | Ch 4: Pinecone Fashion... • Read Pages 14–15 • (MiH)<br>*Made in Heaven*: Worksheet 1 • Pages 111-112 • (TG) | | | |
| | Day 117 | Ch 4: Pinecone Fashion Coming Soon to a Mall Near You<br>*Made in Heaven*: Worksheet 2 • Pages 113–114 • (TG) | | | |
| | Day 118 | Ch 5: Cleaning Like a Lotis Leaf • Read Pages 16-17 • (MiH)<br>*Made in Heaven*: Worksheet 1 • Pages 115–116 • (TG) | | | |
| | Day 119 | Ch 2: • Read Pages 15–17 • (MOS) | | | |
| | Day 120 | | | | |
| **Week 7** | Day 121 | Ch 6: Robosquid and Jet Propulsion<br>Read Pages 18–19 • (MiH)<br>*Made in Heaven*: Worksheet 1 • Pages 117–118 • (TG) | | | |
| | Day 122 | Ch 7: Mantis Shrimp Eye... • Read Pages 20–21 • (MiH)<br>*Made in Heaven*: Worksheet 1 • Pages 119–120 • (TG) | | | |
| | Day 123 | Ch 7: Mantis Shrimp Eye Improves Next Wave of...<br>*Made in Heaven*: Worksheet 2 • Pages 121–122 • (TG) | | | |
| | Day 124 | Ch 3: • Read Pages 19–30 • (MOS) | | | |
| | Day 125 | | | | |
| **Week 8** | Day 126 | Ch 8: Butterflies Prevent... • Read Pages 22–23 • (MiH)<br>*Made in Heaven*: Worksheet 1 • Pages 123–124 • (TG) | | | |
| | Day 127 | ***Made in Heaven*: Ch. 1–8 Quiz 1** • Pages 211–214 • (TG) | | | |
| | Day 128 | Ch 9: Human Eye • Read Pages 24-25 • (MiH)<br>*Made in Heaven*: Worksheet 1 • Pages 125–126 • (TG) | | | |
| | Day 129 | Ch 4: • Read Pages 31–41 • (MOS) | | | |
| | Day 130 | | | | |
| **Week 9** | Day 131 | Ch 9: Human Eye — A Better Camera Lens<br>*Made in Heaven*: Worksheet 2 • Pages 127–128 • (TG) | | | |
| | Day 132 | Ch 10: Computer Virus Software... • Read Pages 26–27 • (MiH)<br>*Made in Heaven*: Worksheet 1 • Pages 129–130 • (TG) | | | |
| | Day 133 | Ch 10: Computer Virus Software...<br>*Made in Heaven*: Worksheet 2 • Pages 131–132 • (TG) | | | |
| | Day 134 | Ch 5: • Read Pages 43–59 • (MOS) | | | |
| | Day 135 | | | | |

| Date | Day | Assignment | Due Date | ✓ | Grade |
|------|-----|------------|----------|---|-------|
| | | Second Semester–Fourth Quarter | | | |
| Week 1 | Day 136 | Ch 11: The Human Brain... • Read Pages 28–29 • (MiH)<br>*Made in Heaven*: Worksheet 1 • Page 133–134 • (TG) | | | |
| | Day 137 | Ch 11: The Human Brain Inspires Faster Computer Chips<br>*Made in Heaven*: Worksheet 2 • Pages 135–136 • (TG) | | | |
| | Day 138 | Ch 12: Anti-Lasers Learn from... • Read Pages 30-31 • (MiH)<br>*Made in Heaven*: Worksheet 1 • Pages 137–138 • (TG) | | | |
| | Day 139 | Ch 6: • Read Pages 61–78 • (MOS) | | | |
| | Day 140 | | | | |
| Week 2 | Day 141 | Ch 13: Decoding the Bombard... • Read Pages 32–33 • (MiH)<br>*Made in Heaven*: Worksheet 1 • Pages 139-140 • (TG) | | | |
| | Day 142 | Ch 13: Decoding the Bombard Beetle<br>*Made in Heaven*: Worksheet 2 • Pages 141–142 • (TG) | | | |
| | Day 143 | Ch 14: Mosquitos Studied for... • Read Pages 34–35 • (MiH)<br>*Made in Heaven*: Worksheet 1 • Pages 143–144 • (TG) | | | |
| | Day 144 | Ch 7: • Read Pages 79–90 • (MOS) | | | |
| | Day 145 | | | | |
| Week 3 | Day 146 | Ch 15: Listen Like a Fly on a Wall • Read Pages 36–37 • (MiH)<br>*Made in Heaven*: Worksheet 1 • Pages 145–146 • (TG) | | | |
| | Day 147 | Ch 15: Listen Like a Fly on a Wall<br>*Made in Heaven*: Worksheet 2 • Pages 147–148 • (TG) | | | |
| | Day 148 | Ch 16: Healing Power of the Body... • Read Pages 38-39 • (MiH)<br>*Made in Heaven*: Worksheet 1 • Pages 149–150 • (TG) | | | |
| | Day 149 | Ch 8: • Read Pages 91–94 • (MOS) | | | |
| | Day 150 | | | | |
| Week 4 | Day 151 | *Made in Heaven*: **Ch. 9–16 Quiz 2** • Pages 215–218 • (TG) | | | |
| | Day 152 | Ch 17: Humans Give Robotic... • Read Pages 40–41 • (MiH)<br>*Made in Heaven*: Worksheet 1 • Pages 151–152 • (TG) | | | |
| | Day 153 | Ch 18: Mussels with Strong... • Read Pages 42–43 • (MiH)<br>*Made in Heaven*: Worksheet 1 • Pages 153–154 • (TG) | | | |
| | Day 154 | Research Report • (MOS) • Worksheet 1 • Pages 155 • (TG) | | | |
| | Day 155 | | | | |
| Week 5 | Day 156 | Ch 19: Velcro® Imagined in the... • Read Pages 44–45 • (MiH)<br>*Made in Heaven*: Worksheet 1 • Pages 157–158 • (TG) | | | |
| | Day 157 | Ch 20: Wasp Nests and... • Read Pages 46–47 • (MiH)<br>*Made in Heaven*: Worksheet 1 • Pages 159–160 • (TG) | | | |
| | Day 158 | Ch 21: Cats Eyes That Saves Lives • Read Pages 48–49 • (MiH)<br>*Made in Heaven*: Worksheet 1 • Pages 161–162 • (TG) | | | |
| | Day 159 | Ch 22: Gecko Feet Help Robots...<br>Read Pages 50–51 • (MiH)<br>*Made in Heaven*: Worksheet 1 • Pages 163–164 • (TG) | | | |
| | Day 160 | | | | |

| Date | Day | Assignment | Due Date | ✓ | Grade |
|------|-----|-----------|----------|---|-------|
| **Week 6** | Day 161 | Ch 22: Gecko Feet Help Robots Go Vertical<br>*Made in Heaven*: Worksheet 2 • Pages 165–166 • (TG) | | | |
| | Day 162 | Ch 23-24: Why Fish.../Fins are... • Read Pages 52–55 • (MiH)<br>*Made in Heaven*: Worksheet 1 • Page 167–168 • (TG) | | | |
| | Day 163 | ***Made in Heaven*: Ch. 17–24 Quiz 3** • Pages 219–220 • (TG) | | | |
| | Day 164 | Ch 25: Termites and.... • Read Pages 56–57 • (MiH)<br>*Made in Heaven*: Worksheet 1 • Pages 169–170 • (TG) | | | |
| | Day 165 | | | | |
| **Week 7** | Day 166 | Ch 25: Termites and Air-Conditioned Buildings<br>*Made in Heaven*: Worksheet 2 • Pages 171–172 • (TG) | | | |
| | Day 167 | Ch 26: Broken Bones, Healing,.... • Read Pages 58–59 • (MiH)<br>*Made in Heaven*: Worksheet 1 • Pages 173–174 • (TG) | | | |
| | Day 168 | Ch 27: Wipers, Eyes, and... • Read Pages 60–61 • (MiH)<br>*Made in Heaven*: Worksheet 1 • Pages 175–176 • (TG) | | | |
| | Day 169 | Ch 27: Wipers, Eyes, and Controversy<br>*Made in Heaven*: Worksheet 2 • Pages 177–178 • (TG) | | | |
| | Day 170 | | | | |
| **Week 8** | Day 171 | Ch 28: Kingfishers Break Sonic... • Read Pages 62–63 • (MiH)<br>*Made in Heaven*: Worksheet 1 • Pages 179–180 • (TG) | | | |
| | Day 172 | Ch 29: Worms at the Center... • Read Pages 64–65 • (MiH)<br>*Made in Heaven*: Worksheet 1 • Pages 181–182 • (TG) | | | |
| | Day 173 | Ch 30: Moth's Eye Inspires New... • Read Pages 66–67 • (MiH)<br>*Made in Heaven*: Worksheet 1 • Pages 183–184 • (TG) | | | |
| | Day 174 | Ch 31: The Astonishing Leaf... • Read Pages 68–69 • (MiH)<br>*Made in Heaven*: Worksheet 1 • Pages 185–186 • (TG) | | | |
| | Day 175 | | | | |
| **Week 9** | Day 176 | Ch 32: Mathematics, Sunflowers... • Read Pages 70–71 • (MiH)<br>*Made in Heaven*: Worksheet 1 • Pages 187–188 • (TG) | | | |
| | Day 177 | Conclusion • Read Pages 72–78 • (MiH) | | | |
| | Day 178 | ***Made in Heaven*: Ch. 25–32 Quiz 4** • Pages 221–224 • (TG) | | | |
| | Day 179 | ***Made in Heaven*: Ch. 1–32 Test** • Pages 225–226 • (TG) | | | |
| | Day 180 | | | | |
| | | Final Grade | | | |

**Applied Engineering Worksheets**

**for Use with**

*Discovery of Design*

## Introduction

1. What is the name of the science where designs are developed from designs in nature?

2. What are the two distinct explanations for the many successful ideas derived from studying nature?

3. What is the major flaw in crediting evolution for the successful design features found in nature?

4. What is the historic definition of science?

5. What are two reasons the Creator deliberately included all the useful design features in our world?

## Bacteria > Micro-motor

1. What was the year of Leeuwenhoek's discovery of "small living creatures in rain water"?

2. How do many microscopic life forms propel themselves through liquids?

3. How many of these motors would fit along a one-inch length?

4. What are the three main parts of these "motors"?

5. Describe how myxobacteria move.

## Digging Deeper

6. What is the precise meaning of the words *micro* and *nano*?

7. How does the speed of an electric fan compare with the 100,000-rpm rate of the molecular motor?

8. What are the chemical properties of silly string?

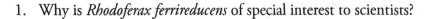
## Bacteria > Battery

1.  Why is *Rhodoferax ferrireducens* of special interest to scientists?

2.  What is the efficiency rate for production of electric energy by *Rhodoferax ferrireducens*?

3.  What are bacterial batteries?

4.  What is the technological challenge toward making bacterial batteries a realistic option for energy-starved areas?

5.  How much sugar would it take to power a 60-watt lightbulb for a number of hours using bacterial batteries?

## Digging Deeper

6.  What actually is a battery?

7.  Why are most energy-conversion processes inefficient?

8.  How many electrons pass through a standard 60-watt light bulb in one second?

## Biofilm > Bacteria Control

1. What are biofilms?

2. How do members of biofilms communicate with one another?

3. What is the ability of biofilms to affect their surroundings by hundreds of chemical compounds called?

4. What is an example of biofilms helping to block invading foreign bacteria?

5. Studies are being done to determine if biofilms can control corrosion in what fuel-related equipment?

## Digging Deeper

6. Estimate the number of bacteria on your hands.

7. Where might one find freshwater biofilms?

8. What are some unusual locations of biofilms?

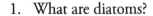
## Diatom > Nanotechnology

1. What are diatoms?

2. Where are diatoms found?

3. Why are scientists who are interested in nanotechnology looking at diatoms?

4. What two chemical substances are used to harden diatom components for use as microscopic mechanical gears?

5. What does the author mean by "designer diatoms"?

## Digging Deeper

6. Are diatoms plants or animals?

7. What is the mineral name for glass?

8. Diatomaceous earth is a powdered form of diatom fossils. What are some of its uses?

## Protein > Solar Cells

1. How do plants capture energy from the sun?



2. Which is more efficient at capturing energy from the sun — plants or silicon solar cells?



3. What part of plants have scientists succeeded in using to create small solar cells?



4. What happens when light shines on the plant-based proteins on an electricity-conducting glass surface?



5. What is one advantage for protein solar energy cells mentioned in the book?



## Digging Deeper

6. How is electric current measured?



7. How is it possible that wind power, water power, and fossil fuels are all forms of solar energy?



8. Can you name three non-solar forms of energy?

## Introduction

1.  Where would one expect to find the approximately 90 percent of distinct living animals on earth that are said to still be unknown to science?

2.  Which word derives from Latin for "something cut in"?

3.  Are insects vertebrate or invertebrate?

4.  Which insect is named in the Bible in Exodus 10:4?

5.  The label "insects" include what types of creatures?

## Ants > Airlines

1. What is the complex, organized behavior you see with a flock of birds called?

2. When it comes to ants, what determines the overall group behavior?

3. How do ants convey information to other ants and what information can be shared?

4. The self-organizing ability of creatures has been modeled with computer programs to do what?

5. These programs are being used in what ways today? Give three examples.

## Digging Deeper

6. How many legs does an ant have?

7. How does the total number of ants compare with other animals?

8. What did King Solomon say about ants?

## Asian Beetle > Paper Whitener

1. Where are several species of brilliant white beetles found?

2. What is the genus name of these white beetles?

3. Instead of pigment, what substance is used to form the translucent surface cells?

4. How does the structure of the fibers forming the scales create the white color?

5. Give one possible application of technology developed from these white beetles.

## Digging Deeper

6. What is currently used to give paper a white color?

7. What is chitin?

8. What could be the purpose of the Cyphochilus beetle's white appearance?

## Bombardier Beetle > Gas Turbine Engine

1. What interesting feature helped give the bombardier beetle its name?

2. How quickly does the bombardier beetle's jet of steam move?

3. What chemical does the beetle's spray and rocket fuel have in common?

4. What problem during aircraft flight is a reason for studying the bombardier beetle?

5. What other designs may be improved by trying to recreate the unique features of the beetle's defense system?

## Digging Deeper

6. Hydrogen peroxide is found in many medicine cabinets. What is its use?

7. Where are bombardier beetles found?

8. How would an evolutionist attempt to explain the origin of the bombardier beetle?

## Butterfly > Cosmetics

1. Which South American butterfly is known by its blue iridescent wings?

2. What process is behind the brilliant color of their wings?

3. What are the other names for what scientists call the process of light and color wavelengths on the wings?

4. What is the process called that cosmetic companies are using to mimic the light wave properties of the butterfly and to replace the use of pigments, dyes, waxes, and oils?

5. What other applications could this technology possibly impact?

## Digging Deeper

6. How many different species of butterflies have been catalogued?

7. How long does a butterfly live?

8. What causes the different colors of light?

## Dragonfly > Surveillance

1.  What physical feature makes dragonflies unusual among insects?

2.  How fast are dragonflies when they are flying forward?

3.  What happens when the dragonfly twists its wings slightly on a downward stroke?

4.  What visual illusion do dragonflies create when they are flying in a direct line with their prey?

5.  What military applications are being considered in relation to the design of the dragonfly?

## Digging Deeper

6.  What becomes of dragonflies in wintertime?

7.  Have fossil dragonflies been found?

8.  What do dragonflies eat?

## Firefly > Light Stick

1. What does a firefly create by mixing chemicals in its abdomen?

2. Oxygen is combined with what substance to activate the reaction?

3. What is the light-producing process by living things called?

4. How many species of fireflies are there?

5. What are the eggs and larvae of the firefly called, which produce a soft green-white light?

## Digging Deeper

6. What is the lifespan of the firefly?

7. What is the origin of the chemical names *luciferin* and *luciferase*?

8. Why does a group of fireflies sometimes blink off and on simultaneously?

## Fly > Hearing Aid

1. Why is a small fly, *Ormia ochracea*, being studied for hearing aid advancements?

2. What is remarkable about how a female *Ormia ochracea* can track down a singing cricket in order to lay its eggs on its back?

3. How do people determine the direction of a sound?

4. Are scientists aware of how the fly is able to distinguish the direction of the cricket's singing with no discernable difference in the sound's arrival time to the fly's ears?

5. What is an additional potential benefit for hearing aids by studying the fly?

## Digging Deeper

6. How may a cricket be used as a thermometer?

7. How does hearing sensitivity compare with our other senses?

8. Does a fly have eardrums?

## Honey Bee > Surveillance

1. What kind of eyes do honeybees, flies, and many other insects have?

2. What are the tiny tubes of columns called that each eye in a honeybee contains?

3. How does light travel through the eye of a bee?

4. What is the process Berkeley scientists are trying to recreate that is based on the design of the honeybee's eye?

5. What are some practical applications mentioned from reproducing the processes of a honeybee's eyes?

## Digging Deeper

6. What image does an insect see with its compound eyes?

7. How small is one of the multiple lenses in the honeybee eye?

8. What is ultraviolet light?

## Insect Hearing > Atomic Force Microscope

1. AFM stands for what type of device and what is its purpose?

2. What is one challenge or problem with the AFM probe?

3. What do insects like grasshoppers or moths hear with their ultra-sensitive listening systems?

4. How is the AFM being used to study the hearing of insects?

5. What is the goal of using the AFM on insects?

## Digging Deeper

6. Who invented the Atomic Force Microscope?

7. How small an object can an AFM clearly "see"?

8. List some of the different types of microscopes.

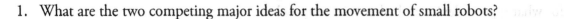

## Insects > Robotics

1.  What are the two competing major ideas for the movement of small robots?

2.  What is the problem with wheels on robotic planet probes like the Mars probe *Opportunity*?

3.  Describe the experiments taking place at the PEDAL lab at Berkeley.

4.  What is the major advantage of small, multi-leg robots over actual insects?

5.  Name two possible applications of robots with insect-inspired legs listed in the book.

## Digging Deeper

6.  What is the origin of the word *robot*?

7.  Can one obtain an advanced degree in robotics?

8.  How many legs do centipedes have?

## Namib Beetle > Water Collector

1.  What is another name for the Namib beetle?

2.  What does the name *Namib* mean?

3.  How does the Namib beetle get water in this very dry region?

4.  How does the beetle "drink" the water collected?

5.  What do the following words mean?

    a. Hydrophilic:_____

    b. Hydrophobic:_____

## Digging Deeper

6.  What causes fog or dew to appear in the morning?

7.  What defines a desert climate?

8.  How do Namib beetles communicate?

## Spider Silk > Fiber Optics

1. How thin can a spider thread be?

2. Why do spiders spin these threads?

3. What are nanotubes used for? Give two examples.

4. What are two unknowns about spiders and their threads?

5. Why is synthetic spider silk one of the most sought after technologies in biomimicry?

## Digging Deeper

6. What was an early use of spider silk by astronomers?

7. What is a nanotube?

8. How can it be said that spider silk is stronger than steel?

## Termite Mound > Ventilation

1. Why are the termite mounds built by *Macrotermes michaelseni* of interest to architects?


2. Why is temperature a concern for these termites?


3. How do termites maintain the temperature of the termite mound?


4. In the book, in what country has the Eastgate Building been constructed using design inspired by termites?


5. Why does the Eastgate Building only use 10 percent of the energy that a conventionally built one would?


## Digging Deeper

6. How many termites may live in a single African mound?


7. Describe how the termite mound heating and cooling vents operate.


8. What is the average temperature of Zimbabwe's capital city, Harare?

## Timber Beetle Larva > Chainsaw

1. What is another name for the larvae of the timber beetle?

2. What feature do the larvae have that enables them to chew through wood?

3. Who designed the chipper chain?

4. What is another name for the chipper chain?

5. Why was Cox's invention so popular?

## Digging Deeper

6. How were big trees harvested before chainsaws were invented?

7. Are timber beetles a major pest in forestry?

8. What is the largest commercial chainsaw manufactured today?

## Wasp > Paper

1. Why was paper so expensive centuries ago?

2. Which inventor took inspiration from a nest of paper wasps to develop a new way of making paper?

3. What raw materials were used to make the wasp nests?

4. In modern paper mills, what kind of fibers from the wood are separated from their lignin binder?

5. What is added to the fibers to make wood pulp?

## Digging Deeper

6. What is the shape of the paper wasp nest?

7. What is lignin?

8. Is some paper still made from linen cloth?

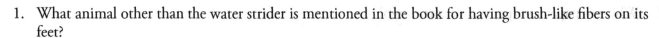

## Water Strider > Water Repellant

1.  What animal other than the water strider is mentioned in the book for having brush-like fibers on its feet?

2.  What theory of how the water striders stay dry while "walking on water" was proven incorrect?

3.  What is the scientific name for the thousands of tiny hairs on the water strider's feet in which air is trapped and creates a water-repellent barrier?

4.  Researchers in China discovered that the barrier worked so well, it took how many times the normal weight of a water strider before the artificial water strider leg penetrated the water's surface?

5.  What are two potential applications of utilizing the waters strider's amazing features?

## Digging Deeper

6.  How do water striders move from one pond or puddle to another?

7.  How is it that a water strider, or even a needle, can float on water?

8.  How do water striders move so rapidly on water?

## Bat > Sonar Systems

1. What voice is "heard in our land" from Song of Solomon 2:12?


2. What is the process called that bats use to locate prey after dark using sound?


3. What is the normal frequency range for human hearing?


4. What is the name of the strategy bats use to catch insects?


5. What does the word "sonar" stand for?


## Digging Deeper

6. What actually is a sound wave, as produced by bats?


7. What is the frequency of a dog whistle?


8. What is a flying fox?

## Bird Flight > Aircraft

1. Turbulence created by the wings and tail feathers of birds is known as what?

2. What is the problem if birds fly too quickly? What if they fly too slowly?

3. What is the mathematical formula that describes bird flight?

4. A Strouhal number for efficient flight ranges between what numbers?

5. What do engineers use the flight-swim formula for?

## Digging Deeper

6. What are the fastest speeds for animals in the air and under water?

7. Give a numerical example for the bird flight formula.

8. Do flying fish have wings?

## Flying Reptile > Delta Wing Aircraft

1. In terms of design, how was the flying reptile *Sharovipteryx mirabilis* different from today's flying vertebrates?

2. What was noted as a side benefit for this design in *Sharovipteryx mirabilis*?

3. What is the small triangular wing structure up in the front of both the fossil lizard and modern aircraft?

4. How does the design of *Sharovipteryx mirabilis* create a problem for evolutionists?

5. Why were the Wright brothers successful in their design while da Vinci was not?

## Digging Deeper

6. What is the meaning of the name *Sharovipteryx mirabilis* given to the fossil flying reptile?

7. What is a wind tunnel?

8. What year did the Wright brothers succeed with their flight?

## Kingfisher > Bullet Train

1. Japanese trains can travel in excess of what speed?

2. What problem did Japan's rail system have that scientists looked to the kingfisher to solve?

3. What happens to the kingfisher when it dives for fish because of its ingenious beak's design?

4. What is a bonus for the train engine's design that mimics the kingfisher's bill?

5. What other feature of some trains owe their design to this amazing bird?

## Digging Deeper

6. Where do kingfishers live?

7. How do kingfishers see while under water?

8. What is a sonic boom caused by the bullet trains?

## Owl Wing > Noise Reduction

1. What two design features help owls to catch prey by surprise?

2. Owls have what kind of special feathers that allow flight at slow, quiet speeds?

3. Why is the military interested in making aircraft quieter? What about commercial aviation?

4. The use of owl-feather technology may allow for what?

5. Why would a retractable brush-like fringe on airplane wings, and a velvety coating on the landing gear not be considered complete successes?

## Digging Deeper

6. What is the largest owl?

7. How many species of owl have been catalogued?

8. How is the loudness of sound measured?

## Swift > Aircraft Wings

1. What are some things swifts do while flying?

2. About how many trips to the moon does a swift fly the equivalent of over a lifetime?

3. What makes it possible for swifts to perform acrobatic moves while flying?

4. Who are studying models of swift wings in wind tunnels?

5. What is NASA testing?

## Digging Deeper

6. How does evolution explain the origin of flight?

7. Since swifts do not perch on tree branches, where do they build their nests?

8. Are swifts and swallows the same?

## Toucan Beak > Shock Absorber

1. How does the length of the toco toucan's beak compare to the height of its body?

2. What seemingly should happen when the bird uses its long beak to reach tree fruits that are far away?

3. How does the weight of the beak compare to the bird's total weight?

4. Describe the design of the toucan's beak.

5. Name two potential uses the toucan's beak may provide as a model.

## Digging Deeper

6. In which countries might you find toucans?

7. Why are toucans so colorful?

8. How can the beak of a woodpecker survive hammering?

## Boxfish > Automobile Design

1. Who looks to nature for guidance in new automobile designs?

2. What surprising fish caught the attention of engineers?

3. Describe the skin of a boxfish.

4. What has DaimlerChrysler built that copies the overall shape of the boxfish?

5. What are the door panels patterned after?

## Digging Deeper

6. How large is the boxfish?

7. Where is the boxfish found?

8. How many distinct species of boxfish have been catalogued?

## Brittlestar > Microlens

1. What are echinoderms?

2. What covers the brittlestar's outer skeletal surface?

3. How does calcite help the brittlestar?

4. How did God design the brittlestar to deal with the problem birefringence?

5. What have the engineers at Bell Labs concluded about the design of the microlenses of the brittlestar?

## Digging Deeper

6. Where in the oceans are brittlestars found?

7. What does evolution theory suggest about the origin of vision?

8. Besides the lenses of brittlestars, where else might one find the mineral calcite?

## Cuttlefish > Camouflage

1. Describe the cuttlefish.

2. Describe how a cuttlefish quickly changes color.

3. Describe how a cuttlefish can reflect the color of its nearby environment.

4. What has the military prepared based on the color-changing design of the cuttlefish?

5. How may the use of polarized light patterns on the skin help cuttlefish?

## Digging Deeper

6. Name some animals that change color.

7. Are cuttlefish used as seafood?

8. What is polarized light?

## Elephant Nose Fish > Electric Sensor

1.  What can the elephant nose fish generate and detect and how does this help the fish?

2.  How can the elephant nose fish design be applied to air bag deployment safety?

3.  What other applications can be borrowed from the design of the elephant nose fish?

4.  Describe the communication abilities of the ghost knifefish.

5.  How does the military mimic the knifefish?

## Digging Deeper

6.  What is an electric field?

7.  Does an electric eel also generate an electric field?

8.  What large sea animal has a nose protrusion somewhat similar to the elephant nose fish?

## Fish Motion > Ship Propulsion

1. What is an important goal for ships?

2. What two distinct advantages do fish have for their propulsion?

3. What chemical is promising for providing a slippery surface for boats?

4. What unexpected discovery involving whale flippers may have potential application for airplanes and helicopters?

5. How do competitive swimmers benefit from the study of fish design?

## Digging Deeper

6. How does the speed of Olympic swimmers compare with fish?

7. Is it known why whales breach, or leap above the water?

8. What is the supposed evolutionary origin of whales?

## Lobster Eye > Telescope Lens

1. How do most animals and people focus light?

2. How does a lobster eye work?

3. What has copied the lobster's eye design?

4. Why are ordinary lenses or mirrors not suitable for the focusing of x-rays?

5. When used for laboratory use, what does the lobster lens generate when it functions in reverse?

## Digging Deeper

6. What is an x-ray?

7. What do x-ray telescopes see?

8. Is the crayfish eye similar to that of a lobster?

## Mussels > Adhesive

1. Why is the adhesive produced by mussels remarkable?

2. What surprising element is found in mussel-glue? Why is it so surprising?

3. What key glue ingredient isolated from mussels has been used to bond human tissue after surgery?

4. What may lead to precise surgical sealants in eye surgery?

5. What could lead to solvents that will dissolve it when needed?

## Digging Deeper

6. Why are mussels a problem in inland waters?

7. What does the term *biodegradable* mean?

8. Who invented superglue?

## Octopus > Robotics

1.  Can octopus tentacles gently wrap around objects?

2.  Can octopus tentacles stiffen to transfer prey from one location to another?

3.  How is an octopus arm similar to a human arm?

4.  What do scientists recognize about the octopus arm?

5.  How does a flexible robotic arm improve function?

## Digging Deeper

6.  Does an octopus regenerate a lost arm?

7.  How long can octopus arms grow?

8.  What kinds of robotic arms are currently used in space?

## Seashell > Construction Material

1. What makes up the structure of seashells, resulting in shells that are hard, strong, and flexible?

2. What makes up the "bricks and mortar" structure of seashells?

3. How many microscopic layers does a shell have?

4. What kind of medical applications do scientists hope to achieve by copying the design of the seashell?

5. What larger scale applications do scientists hope to achieve?

## Digging Deeper

6. What is the origin of the name *mother-of-pearl*?

7. What materials are currently used for artificial bone?

8. What are some traditional uses of shell material?

## Sea Slug > Chemicals

1. What are see slugs and how big are they?

2. What do some sea slugs do when they are threatened by a predator?

3. What does the aplysia sea slug spray outward when disturbed?

4. What function do scientists believe the anti-microbial chemical protein detected in sea slugs have in addition to repelling certain predators?

5. Where do scientists hope sea slug protein may serve to prevent the growth of bacteria and other unwanted microbes?

## Digging Deeper

6. How many species of sea slug are known to exist?

7. What does the term *microbe* refer to?

8. What are some descriptive sea slug names?

## Sea Sponge > Fiber Optics

1. What is the Venus Flower Basket and where does it typically live?

2. What two advantages does the Venus Flower Basket's optical fibers have over man-made fiber optics strands?

3. What is the result of these two advantages?

4. What is a major problem with commercial optical fiber?

5. What is symbiosis?

## Digging Deeper

6. What is the composition of man-made optical fiber?

7. Have fossil sponges been found?

8. Besides the mutual benefit between the Flower Basket and shrimp, give some other examples of symbiosis.

## Whale > Submarine

1. What challenges do designers of submarines face?


2. What shape does a submarine resemble?


3. What does the blunt nose of both sperm whales and submarines result in?


4. What part of a whale are rear propulsion with propellers somewhat equivalent to?


5. What other whale system is utilized by modern submarines?


## Digging Deeper

6. What is the largest whale?


7. How deep can whales dive?


8. How do whales communicate with each other?

## Ankylosaurus > Fiberglass

1. Were animals living in the distant past primitive and simple?

2. How was the ankylosaurus' armor plating different from crocodiles?

3. How do the fibers of the ankylosaurus' armor plating resemble fiberglass?

4. What benefit did the ankylosaurus have from its own form of organic fiberglass?

5. What highway improvement has been proposed that is based on the creative design of the ankylosaurus?

## Digging Deeper

6. How large were dinosaur eggs?

7. How many dinosaur species have been discovered?

8. When was fiberglass invented?

## Antler > Organ Repair

1. What ability do reptiles and amphibians have?

2. How many times slower is human fingernail growth than deer antler growth?

3. What are scientists studying about antler regeneration?

4. What appear to be directly involved in the process of antler regeneration?

5. To what may the further understanding of antler growth lead?

## Digging Deeper

6. Which animal holds the record size for antlers?

7. How is antler size related to animal age?

8. What are stem cells?

## Dog Paw > Shoe Soles

1. What problem did Paul Sperry encounter?

2. What did Sperry observe about his dog's paws?

3. What did Sperry cut into the thick sheet of rubber?

4. What did this pattern allow the shoes to do?

5. What did Sperry manufacture?

## Digging Deeper

6. Where else besides shoe soles is the herringbone pattern found?

7. How have Paul Sperry's ideas been applied to automobiles?

8. Where can one learn more about Paul Sperry's discovery?

## Gecko > Adhesive

1. What acrobatic abilities do geckos have?

2. What does a microscope show about the toes of a gecko?

3. The gecko uses two "sticking" forces. What are they?

4. How does the design of the gecko solve the moisture problem scientists have found with the gecko tape they have created?

5. How may improved gecko tape be useful?

## Digging Deeper

6. Explain the nature of van der Waals and capillary forces.

7. Who invented post-it notes?

8. How do spiders and other insects walk on ceilings?

## Giraffe > Antigravity Spacesuit

1. What is fluid shift?

2. Why are some astronauts plagued with fainting spells for several days when they return to earth?

3. How does a giraffe keep from fainting when raising and lowering its head several feet?

4. What are astronaut spacesuits and military flight suit designs based on?

5. How are the suits designed to prevent fainting?

## Digging Deeper

6. What exercise activity of orbiting astronauts counters "fluid shift"?

7. How tall is an adult giraffe?

8. How large is the giraffe heart?

## Horse Bone > Construction

1.  How thick is the lower bone of a horse leg?

2.  What unexpected feature does the metacarpus have that should weaken the structure?

3.  How did God design the metacarpus to remain strong?

4.  What have scientists found when they have modeled the horse bone and then applied pressure?

5.  What have scientists found is the result of varying the type of material used around openings in structures?

## Digging Deeper

6.  Do we have any bones with a foramen opening, similar to the horse?

7.  What is the top speed of a racehorse?

8.  How much stress is generated in the bones of athletes?

## Penguin Eye > Sunglasses

1. Do penguins have poor vision under the intense glare of polar sunlight?

2. What filters blue and ultraviolet colors of the solar spectrum for penguins?

3. What other kinds of birds filter color in this way?

4. What do welders use that is based on the design of penguins?

5. What do orange-tinted sunglasses offer pilots, sailors, and skiers?

## Digging Deeper

6. Where in the world are wild penguins found?

7. How large are penguins?

8. What is it about the color orange that makes a useful light filter?

## Tree Frog > Automobile Tires

1. What are tree frogs able to cling to?

2. How is the holding ability of frogs distinct from that of the gecko?

3. These bumps or "cleats" make contact with the leaf surface and cling by what is called "_____."

4. What other way does a frog attract force, allowing it to stick to a leaf?

5. What dual mechanisms allow tree frogs to hang upside-down on leaves, regardless of whether the surface is dry, wet, smooth, or rough?

## Digging Deeper

6. In what regions do tree frogs live?

7. How do tree frogs act as barometers?

8. How many species of frogs are known in the world?

## Body Odor > Insect Repellent

1. Do people attract mosquitoes equally?

2. What do mosquitoes zero in on?

3. According to British research, what prevents mosquitoes from finding some people?

4. How many distinct repellant compounds have researchers found?

5. What could the laboratory identification of repellant compounds lead to?

## Digging Deeper

6. Which mosquitoes bite, the males or females?

7. What chemicals are typically used in insect repellants?

8. What is a major worldwide danger of mosquitoes?

## DNA > Computer Memory

1. Where is DNA found?

2. What does DNA consist of?

3. What do the arrangements of smaller units spaced along the DNA serve?

4. How much information does a single gram of DNA hold?

5. What do scientists hope DNA can help with in the future?

## Digging Deeper

6. What does DNA stand for?

7. What is the size of a DNA molecule?

8. What do the letters stand for in Einstein's formula $E = mc^2$ ?

## Eardrum > Earphone

1. How thin is the eardrum?

2. What does the eardrum vibrate in response to?

3. What motivated Bell's research for ways to transmit the various frequencies or vibrations of the human voice?

4. Describe how the ear processes sound as noted by Bell.

5. Bell described the principle of what two useful items?

## Digging Deeper

6. What were some of Alexander Graham Bell's other inventions?

7. What are the names of the three bones in our inner ear?

8. How was Alexander Graham Bell honored at his death on August 14, 1922?

## Eye Iris > Identification

1.  What do fingerprints provide?

2.  How many measurable characteristics do fingerprints display?

3.  How many identifiable characteristics does an iris have?

4.  Can you tamper with the identifiable characteristics of the iris?

5.  What may someday be commonplace for secure identification purposes?

## Digging Deeper

6.  How does the iris control incoming light to the eye?

7.  What are some ways to express the number $10^{78}$?

8.  Where is iris recognition currently used for security?

## Fibrin > Elastic

1. How are vessels near a wound sealed off?

2. What is the key to the clotting mechanism?

3. How does a clot form?

4. When researchers studied fibrin fibers, what happened when individual fibers were grasped with a device and tension force was applied?

5. What other protein fiber in nature is known to have this extreme stretching ability?

## Digging Deeper

6. What is hemophilia?

7. How does Coumadin affect blood clotting?

8. How is the blood-clotting mechanism related to intelligent design?

## Fingerprint > Prosthetic Hand

1. Do scientists completely understand fingerprints?

2. What are two purposes of fingerprints?

3. How much more sensitive is a grooved surface compared to a smooth one?

4. What are the purposes of the elliptical swirls of a fingerprint?

5. What may studying fingerprints lead to?

## Digging Deeper

6. Is every fingerprint unique?

7. What typical frequencies do our fingerprints detect?

8. Do primates have fingerprints similar to people?

## Leg Bone > Eiffel Tower

1. What is the base of the Eiffel Tower designed after?

2. What is unusual about how the ball joint fits into the hip socket?

3. Who studied the lattice bone ridges within the femur head, called trabeculae?

4. Who later generated a mathematical model of the femur design?

5. Who used a femur model to design a famous tower?

## Digging Deeper

6. What is the largest bone in the human body?

7. How much does the Eiffel Tower weigh?

8. How many people visit the Eiffel Tower each year?

## Muscles > Robotics

1. What is a problem of mechanical arms of current robotic devices?

2. How are our own arms better than mechanical arms?

3. What permits controlled rotation and flexing of our arms?

4. What causes slight expansion or contraction of length in laboratory models?

5. Is it easy to duplicate the muscles within our bodies?

## Digging Deeper

6. How many muscles are in the human body?

7. Which metals have the largest thermal expansion?

8. How much weight is an adult capable of lifting?

## Saliva > Healing

1. What does the common phrase to "lick one's own wounds" mean?

2. Who studied the chemical compounds in human saliva?

3. What did the researchers find?

4. Do small cuts inside the mouth tend to heal more or less quickly than external injuries?

5. Why are histatins now emphasized in medical treatment rather than growth factors?

## Digging Deeper

6. Would not saliva infect an open wound?

7. Why do animals sometimes lick their wounds?

8. How was the healing property of histatin verified?

## Skin > Self-repairing Plastic

1. What is the skin's outer layer called?

2. When the epidermis is injured, what does the inner dermal layer rush to the cut to begin the healing process?

3. What benefit is there to a blood clot forming?

4. How can aircraft components and medical implants heal themselves?

5. How long can this kind of mending take place?

## Digging Deeper

6. How many square feet of skin does an adult have?

7. What is plastic surgery?

8. Is artificial skin available in medicine?

## Tooth Enamel > Armor Coating

1. Name the strongest material in our bodies.

2. How thick is the enamel that covers our teeth?

3. What does the pliable dentin material beneath the enamel layer do?

4. What problem do dentists see with the fillings, crowns, and implants that they use to mimic tooth enamel?

5. What would improve many product surfaces?

## Digging Deeper

6. What is the composition of tooth enamel?

7. Did George Washington have wooden false teeth?

8. What material is used in making modern artificial teeth?

## Vernix > Skin Cream

1. What is the skin of an infant covered with before birth?

2. What does vernix provide a barrier to both before and during childbirth?

3. What does vernix also prevent at birth?

4. How much water is vernix made of?

5. Vernix contains high levels of what vitamin?

## Digging Deeper

6. What is the origin of the name *vernix caseosa*?

7. Do animals also produce vernix?

8. What is ultraviolet light?

## Beech Leaf > Space Antenna

1. How does the beech leaf unfold?

2. What art form resembles the folding of a beech leaf?

3. Where else can we find folding patterns in nature?

4. How would a map work that is based on the folds of a beech leaf?

5. Why would scientists want to fold satellite solar panels?

## Digging Deeper

6. What is the origin of the word *origami*?

7. How does a butterfly unfold its wings?

8. Is there an example of a building structure based on origami?

## Chemicals > Medicine

1.  What percentage of modern drugs originally come from plants or plant derivatives?

2.  How many plants has the U.S. National Cancer Institute identified from which anti-cancer drugs can be made?

3.  What is the field of study where the medical use of specific plants is learned from native societies such as American Indians and Australian aborigines?

4.  What percentage of tropical forest plants have been studied for their chemical compounds?

5.  What is the field of study called where scientists study how animals self-medicate using plant or mineral materials?

## Digging Deeper

6.  How was aspirin discovered?

7.  What actually is aspirin?

8.  Does Scripture comment on plant use for healing?

## Cocklebur > Velcro

1.  What did Swiss engineer Georges de Mestral invent based on the close inspection of cockleburs?

2.  What is the Velcro® fastener made of?

3.  What does Velcro® replace?

4.  What are "mems" and what do they offer?

5.  Where else can we see an example of a Velcro® type fastener in nature?

## Digging Deeper

6.  What are some novel uses of Velcro?

7.  How strong is Velcro?

8.  Where is Velcro Valley?

## Fava Bean > Valve

1. What are fava beans also known as?

2. What were fava beans commonly used for in early Europe?

3. What do forisomes do within the capillary tubes of the bean plant?

4. The internal fluid flow is quickly turned on or off based on the concentration of what in the bean plant fluid?

5. What further uses may the study of forisome fluid control affect?

## Digging Deeper

6. What is the origin of the name *fava*?

7. What are fava beans used for today?

8. What is an unusual use for fava beans?

## Fescue Grass > Herbicide

1. What do homeowners and farmers wage a constant battle against?

2. What is there a heavy reliance on?

3. What is the behavior called where plants generate chemical defenses against competing plants?

4. How does Intrigue, a type of fescue grass, inhibit common lawn weeds?

5. What other plant gives off a chemical that discourages competing plants?

## Digging Deeper

6. What is the most-used herbicide worldwide?

7. What are some examples of allelopathy?

8. What are some varieties of fescue grass?

## Lotus Flower > Surface Cleaner

1. Name one distinction of the lotus flower.


2. What reason did German scientists discover for this "lotus effect" in the 1990s?


3. Explain what happens to droplets of water when they fall onto a lotus plant.


4. What are surfaces called that readily shed water?


5. What did the German chemical company, BASF, create by duplicating the lotus leaf surface?


## Digging Deeper

6. What is the origin of the name *sacred lotus*?


7. What does the seed head of the water lily resemble?


8. What is surface tension?

## Osage Orange > Barbed Wire

1. What did pioneers on the North American prairies use for livestock fences?

2. Who patented an early form of barbed wire and when?

3. What was the first barbed wire business called?

4. How much barbed wire is consumed in the U.S. currently?

5. How many miles long does that equal?

## Digging Deeper

6. Does Osage Orange produce edible fruit?

7. Where might one find a "barbed wire museum"?

8. What is razor wire?

## Pine Cone > Smart Clothes

1. 1. What does the term "smart clothing" refer to?

2. How does the clothing adjust?

3. What inspired the creation of smart clothing?

4. Where were smart clothes first developed and for what?

5. What biomimicry expert is credited with developing smart clothing?

## Digging Deeper

6. Are some pine cones opened only by fire?

7. Why do some pine cones open up when warm and dry, and close again when wet and cold?

8. What are some future plans for smart clothes?

## Rubber Tree > Automobile Tires

1. What did Christopher Columbus notice on one of his several sailing voyages to North America?

2. What did Christopher Columbus learn about the ball?

3. What did European visitors realize the material was useful for?

4. Explain how the substance got the name "rubber."

5. What did Charles Goodyear add to tree gum to improve the material's strength and durability? What is this process called?

## Digging Deeper

6. How is tree gum obtained from the rubber tree?

7. Besides pencil erasure, what other great discovery was made by Joseph Priestley?

8. How does sulfur benefit the durability of rubber?

## Skunk Cabbage > Thermostat

1.  How many species of plants are able to generate body heat somewhat similar to warm-blooded animals?

2.  What ability does skunk cabbage have?

3.  What purpose does the plant's heat generation serve in the summer?

4.  What is a potential application of the skunk cabbage?

5.  Who has succeeded in regulating an electric heater using a feedback mechanism suggested by the skunk cabbage mechanism?

## Digging Deeper

6.  Describe the odor of the skunk cabbage.

7.  Besides the skunk cabbage, what other plant is known for its offensive odor?

8.  How does a thermostat bimetallic strip function?

## Spinach > Solar Cell

1. Name the process whereby plants collect and use sunlight.

2. What does photosynthesis do?

3. How have scientists tapped into the ability of plants in the manufacture of solar cells?

4. What advantages are there to protein-based solar cells over silicon cells?

5. What is the goal of scientists working in the fields of photochemistry and molecular electronics?

## Digging Deeper

6. What is the chemical equation for photosynthesis?

7. How do silicon solar cells work?

8. What is the potential of solar energy on earth?

## Venus Flytrap > Food Packaging

1.  What is the mechanism called that the Venus flytrap uses to trap unwary insects?

2.  What triggers the instant collapse of the Venus flytrap leaf?

3.  How does the Venus flytrap prevent false alarms?

4.  What food packaging application could be created by polymers mimicking the Venus flytrap?

5.  What medical application could be created by polymers mimicking the Venus flytrap?

## Digging Deeper

6.  Where do Venus flytrap plants grow?

7.  What other plants are carnivorous, or insectivorous, besides the Venus flytrap?

8.  Do flytraps ever catch animals larger than insects?

## Water Lily > Construction

1.  When and where did the first World's Fair take place?

2.  Who did the engineers and architects lose out to in the design competition for the central display hall?

3.  What was the building design based on?

4.  On what pattern of support did Paxton base the Crystal Palace?

5.  What was the size of the shell of the Crystal Palace?

## Digging Deeper

6.  What is the origin of the name *Victoria amazonica*?

7.  What was inside the Crystal Palace?

8.  What is the water lily vein pattern?

## Wild Wheat > Humidity Sensor

1. What secret does wheat owe its success?

2. What are the two fibers called that extend outward from the wheat seed?

3. What ensures that the wheat seed can only move downward, into the ground, and not pull loose?

4. Why do scientists suggest the wheat fiber mechanism be copied?

5. How does the filaree plant push its seed into the soil?

## Digging Deeper

6. How does wild and domestic wheat differ?

7. What are some common names for wheat varieties?

8. Where is the filaree plant found?

## Buckyballs > Micro Ball Bearings

1. When was a new variety of carbon discovered?

2. What does the intricate pattern of the newly discovered carbon resemble?

3. Who popularized geodesic domes in his building designs?

4. What are buckyballs currently used as?

5. What new chemical form of carbon was discovered in 1991?

## Digging Deeper

6. What is the geometric shape on the surface of soccer balls and buckyballs?

7. How does the size of a buckyball compare with the period at the end of a sentence?

8. What is the benefit of an architectural geodesic dome?

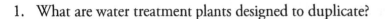

## Nanoparticles > Water Purifier

1. What are water treatment plants designed to duplicate?

2. How many deaths of children are estimated each year due to water-borne pathogens?

3. How does nano-scale technology offer promising solutions to the water-borne pathogen problem?

4. What kind of particles are found to be especially effective cleaning agents?

5. How many square feet of total outside area does a single handful of fine dust of nano-particles contain?

## Digging Deeper

6. Which countries are in special need of clean water?

7. Do some bacteria "eat" oil spills?

8. One nano iron particle, the size of the finest dust, contains how many iron atoms?

## Opal > Photonic Device

1. What is the source of iridescent colors of opals?

2. What causes the colorful flashes from the opal?

3. What are materials called that selectively reflect distinct colors of light?

4. How are laboratory created, synthetic opals being used?

5. What are photonic crystals able to control?

## Digging Deeper

6. Where are natural opals found?

7. What is lithography?

8. How can a computer operate using light pulses?

## Pulsar > Time Standard

1. What are pulsars?

2. Why are pulsars called neutron stars?

3. How much could a spoonful of pulsar "stardust" easily weigh?

4. Who discovered the first pulsar?

5. How are pulsars useful?

## Digging Deeper

6. What is the typical density of a neutron star?

7. How close to earth is the nearest known pulsar?

8. What would happen if we visited a neutron star?

## Water Flow > Impeller & Conclusion

1. What are three examples of the spiral shape found in nature?

2. Why is the twisting spiral motion being studied?

3. What benefits do the engineer-designed impeller blades from PAX have?

4. What are some of the practical uses for the PAX impeller blades?

5. What is planned for many devices, ranging from computers to refrigerators?

## Digging Deeper

6. Is there a mathematical formula for the spiral designs found in nature?

7. How does an impeller differ from a propeller?

8. What is the largest spiral observed in nature?

**Applied Engineering Worksheets**

**for Use with**

***Made in Heaven***

**Become an inventor!**

You have completed enough coursework to have learned how many of today's most cutting-edge innovations are inspired by God's designs in nature. As you begin the remainder of this course, you will enjoy doing simple experiments and learn information on the science behind many of these innovations.

Now here is your challenge! Take steps to become an inventor:

1. Start an invention notebook, where you will detail your thoughts, brainstorm ideas, and do rough sketches.

2. Choose something related to nature that you find interesting.

3. Develop an idea for an improvement, innovation, or invention related to this natural design or feature of nature.

4. At the beginning, try to record as many of your thoughts as possible — even if they seem impractical. Try to list at least 8 to 10 ideas.

5. Next, look at your ideas and see which ones are really needed and can be a practical help. This is where you narrow it down from the improbable to the practical. Try to list at least three of the most practical ideas. If needed, you can do simple drawings where you try to determine whether an idea is doable or not.

6. From these three ideas, choose the one you feel is most viable or able to be done. This is your proposed invention!

7. Now imagine what it would take for your idea to become a workable invention.

8. Create a plan for how you could possibly test out your idea in terms of making it an invention.

9. List three to five reasons for why your invention is needed.

10. Then present either a project notebook with a two-page presentation of your idea and your thoughts, or you can create a simple display on a poster.

## Concepts and Definitions

The following information will lay a critical foundation for related Applied Learning activities. It is important that you read and understand this information so the Applied Learning opportunities can demonstrate and clarify important scientific concepts in action.

Fluid dynamics may sound like a science that is limited to fluid or water. But did you know that any object that moves through air or in water experiences the same aerodynamic effects and follows identical principles? It's true. Fluid does not mean liquids; rather, any medium such as oil, air, gas, and various liquids that are subject to motion are classified as a "fluid." The only difference is the speed in which an object will travel.

This is due to different fluid densities. Density is defined as the mass (weight) per unit volume. As an example, if you had a gallon of water and a gallon of air, the gallon of water would be heavier. The density of water ($62.4$ lbs/ft$^3$) is much greater than the density of air ($.08$ lbs/ft$^3$).

The science of fluid dynamics is comprehensive and we will not be able to cover all that it entails. Rather, we will focus on the articles from the book *Made in Heaven* that are subject to the laws of fluid dynamics and the following characteristics of fluid flow over an object, which are covered in the book.

### Boundary Layer

This is the thin layer that is adjacent to the surface of an object that is unaffected by either laminar or turbulent flow.

### Laminar Flow

Laminar flow includes all fluid flow that moves over an object that takes on the appearance of smooth flow, parallel to the objects surface. Laminar flow contributes to speed, or flow, of an object. This is the opposite effect of turbulent flow.

### Turbulent Flow

Turbulent flow is all fluid flow that moves in a rough/erratic flow pattern. This is the opposite effect of laminar flow.

### Transition Point

This is the location where the fluid flow transitions from laminar to turbulent flow.

### Streamlines

This is a trace or an outline of the flow pattern around an object that defines the flow characteristics around the object.

### Drag

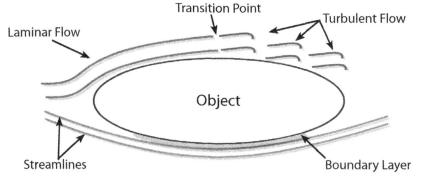

Drag is exactly what it sounds like. Drag slows down and is a hindrance in the flow of fluid.

Q: Which flow type would you expect to exhibit drag?

A: If you said turbulent, then you are correct.

Rough flow — drag, and drag is caused by the shape of the object.

## Applied Learning

The following activity or experiment illustrates important concepts for this portion of the coursework. Please make note of the scientific aspects of the activity as well as the specific areas of focus. These should reinforce important concepts and definitions that you have learned as you apply them.

## Science

Fluid dynamics

## Definition/Focus

Focusing on laminar and turbulent flow
Smooth flow is based on the shape of an object

## Parts Lists

• Hand
• Large container of water, such as a pool or bathtub

## Experiment

In the bathtub or a swimming pool, try to push the water with your hand in the following configurations:

1. An open palm with the fingers tightly pressed together
2. An open palm with your fingers spread apart (as far as you can)
3. Your hand balled up in a fist
4. With the edge of your hand (like a karate chop)

## ☑ Take Away

Note the difference in resistance felt by forming different shapes with your hand in the water. Different shapes exhibit different resistances. Fish are created with a shape that minimizes drag.

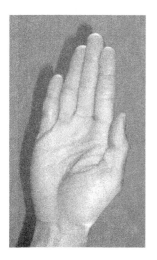 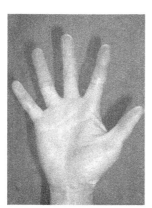 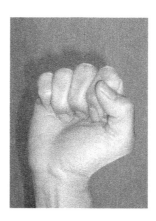 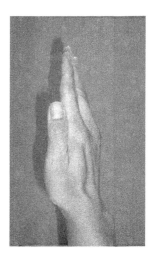

**Questions:**

1. Which shape moved the fastest in water?

2. Why do you think objects of that shape move faster?

3. Can you think of other types of shapes that move with speed?

4. What other examples in God's creation can you think of that might follow this principle?

## Applied Learning

The following activity or experiment illustrates important concepts for this portion of the coursework. Please make note of the scientific aspects of the activity as well as the specific areas of focus. These should reinforce important concepts and definitions that you have learned as you apply them.

## Science

Mechanics of materials (dealing with stress analysis)

## Definition/Focus

The orientation of fibers determine the overall strength of an object

## Parts Lists

- Cardboard (4.5" x 4.5")
- Popsicle sticks (10)
- White glue
- Ruler

## Experiment

You will be gathering together a bunch of popsicle sticks and gluing them on your piece of cardboard. First, look at the direction of the corrugations in the cardboard and glue the popsicle sticks parallel to them. Glue five of them equally spaced apart using white glue.

Once it has dried, gently grab hold of the cardboard with the glued popsicle sticks and try to slowly add pressure to bend it parallel with the popsicle sticks. It should be fairly easy to bend it in this direction.

Next, slowly apply pressure to bend it in the other direction (90 degrees). You will notice that it is difficult to bend, but it is not structurally sound because it is strong in one direction and weak in the other direction.

Engineers want composite structures that are strong in both directions. To accomplish this, glue another row of popsicle sticks 90 degrees to the existing row using the same spacing as before. Proceed with your experiment by bending the cardboard in both directions. Can you see that it is difficult to bend in both directions? You have successfully created a structurally sound composite structure.

## ☑ Take Away

The orientation of the popsicle sticks plays an important role in a structure's overall strength. The arapaima fish has a different orientation of layers that accounts for its incredible armor-like toughness.

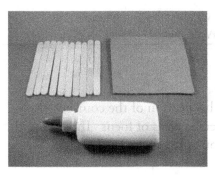 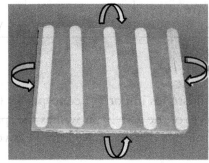 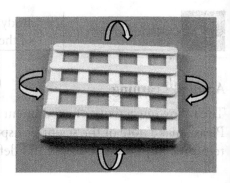

## Questions:

1. Why was the structure weak when the popsicle sticks were initially glued in one direction only on the cardboard?

2. What caused the cardboard to be strong in the other direction?

3. Do you think if the second set of popsicle sticks were glued on a different angle instead of 90 degrees it would make a difference? Why or why not?

## Applied Learning

The following activity or experiment illustrates important concepts for this portion of the coursework. Please make note of the scientific aspects of the activity as well as the specific areas of focus. These should reinforce important concepts and definitions that you have learned as you apply them.

## Science

Materials science

Tensile strength

Stress analysis

## Definition/Focus

Different materials possess different strengths.

## Parts Lists

- Thread (11"–12" long)
- Fishing line (11"–12" long)
- Strip of paper (1" wide x 11" long)
- String (11"–12" long)

## Experiment

Line up the different materials on the parts list. Using gloves, get a good grip and try to pull apart each type of material to the point of breakage (if possible). The amount of effort you put into breaking each material is called tension load.

List (in order) the easiest to the hardest material to break.

## ☑ Take Away

Not all materials break at the same tension load. The seemingly fragile spider silk has a great tensile strength relative to its thickness.

**Questions:**

1. List the test materials that you were able to break. List the ones that did not break.



2. Which material was the easiest to break?



3. Which material was the hardest to break?



4. Can you think of another material that would be really difficult to break?



## Ray Comfort's — Just for Fun!

Take a piece of paper (any size would work) and fold it in half so that the spine of your fold is on the left. Then, about an inch from the fold, tear the paper downward for about two inches (parallel with the fold). Now open the paper and have someone hold his or her thumbs and forefingers — one to the left and one to the right, on the top corners of the torn paper. Then tell the person to pull outward quickly, trying to tear both at the same time.

## Concepts and Definitions

The following information will lay a critical foundation for related Applied Learning activities. It is important that you read and understand this information so the Applied Learning opportunities can demonstrate and clarify important scientific concepts in action.

We are very blessed to have a wide selection of materials available to us for different applications. A material is basically a substance that is natural (raw) or composed (man-made). Materials range from raw matter such as wood to a man-made substance such as paper.

Unfortunately, there does not exist a singular material that does everything for everyone for every task and every job in every circumstance. Comparison of materials is always best when considering the following:

**What:** What am I using it for? What are the best options?

**Where:** Will it be in heat? What if it gets wet?

**When:** Is this a temporary material, or will I need it to last a long time?

**Why:** Consider your task. Will you sacrifice strength for something that is flexible?

**How:** Will this be easy to get/buy? Is it rare or readily available? How much will it cost?

You may not get everything you want in one material when you factor all of the above questions. But the following is a list of some basic properties that are useful for comparison when considering the best material for the task at hand.

### Strength

Strength is the ability of a material to resist breaking when a force is applied. A plastic fork is much easier to break than a metal fork. However, if the weight of the utensil is an issue, the metal fork may not be ideal.

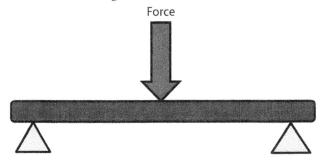

### Elasticity

Elasticity is the ability of a material to deflect and return back to its original shape. Force plays a factor in this. If we use the same force to bend a rubber eraser and a metal hanger, we will probably find different results in elasticity. The rubber eraser will snap back to its original shape, while the metal hanger would yield to a bent shape and not deflect back to its original shape.

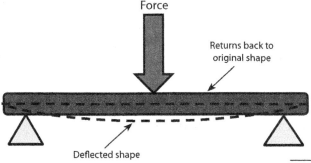

## Tensile Strength

Tensile strength is the ability of a material to stretch without breaking. Compare the amount of force it would take (pulling end to end) to break. You will notice a difference if you try this with the following:

- Hair
- Thread
- Rope

Force ←——————————————————→ Force

## Temperature

Temperature is the melting point of a material.

Example of temperature melting points:

**Aluminum** = 1220 degrees Fahrenheit

**Lead** = 621 degrees Fahrenheit

## Material Classifications

There are various material classifications that help us group like (similar) materials together. We come across them every day and rely on them in so many different ways that you may not have thought of before. Here are a few examples of material classifications.

**Metals** > Steel, copper, silver, gold

**Polymers** > Plastics, rubber, hair, nails, Silly Putty™, styrofoam, plastic

**Ceramics** > Bowls, plates, bricks, pipes, floor tiles

**Semiconductors** > Silicon, gallium, and arsenide

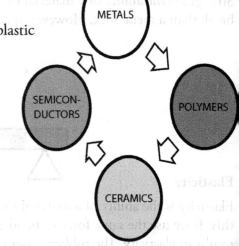

## NOTE:

This section is to provide the reader with a starting point to material sciences. There are many other material properties and classifications that have not been discussed in this study guide. Understanding the properties of a material will enable you to choose the best one for the task at hand. It will give you insight to why a certain material is incorporated when examining man-made products such as the ones in the book *Made in Heaven*.

Material science is complex and far-reaching to a broad science base. It provides us with clever solutions to address new design requirements and create something new.

## Applied Learning

The following activity or experiment illustrates important concepts for this portion of the coursework. Please make note of the scientific aspects of the activity as well as the specific areas of focus. These should reinforce important concepts and definitions that you have learned as you apply them.

## Science

Materials science

## Definition/Focus

Water absorption and contraction

## Parts Lists

- Kitchen sink sponge (3" x 3")
- Piece of paper (3" x 3")
- Hair dryer
- Small towel

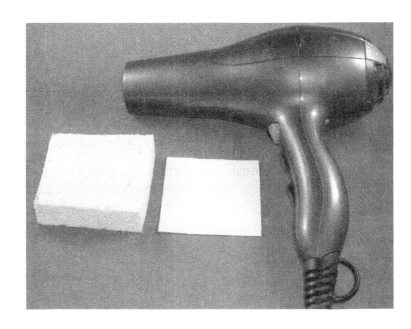

## Experiment

Put each item in your hand. Consider the weight of both the paper and sponge. Next you will be completely saturating the kitchen sponge, then the piece of paper with water. Note the difference in weight compared to when they were both dry. Place the items on a towel and using your hair dryer, dry both pieces at the same time.

## ☑ Take Away

When water is removed from a material, the material will contract and change its shape, and the result is a stiffer item. When water is added, the material stretches and becomes softer. Pinecones use this same principle in order to spread their seed as humidity decreases in the air.

Questions:

1. Was there a difference in the shape of the piece of paper after you dried it, compared to its original state at the beginning of the experiment?

2. What about the sponge? Was there a difference in shape after using the hair dryer to take out the excess water?

3. Did both the paper and sponge take the same amount of time to completely dry?

## Applied Learning

The following activity or experiment illustrates important concepts for this portion of the coursework. Please make note of the scientific aspects of the activity as well as the specific areas of focus. These should reinforce important concepts and definitions that you have learned as you apply them.

## Science

Structural mechanics

## Definition/Focus

Cantilever and contact area

Geometric shapes of contact areas

## Parts Lists

- Piece of paper (8.5 x 11)
- Ping-pong ball

## Experiment

Fold a piece of paper in three equal parts (widths — like a triangle when viewed from the side)

Hold the folded paper on the short end and place a ping-pong ball on top nearest your hand. See if you can keep the ping-pong ball from falling off the paper.

## ☑ Take Away

With the ping-pong ball sitting on top of the paper, what we perceive as being a smooth piece of paper is, in fact, a coarse microscopic surface. The ping-pong ball is unable to firmly plant itself because of its coarse surface, which is due to the reduced contact area between the ball and the paper. Another aspect of the instability is the fact that the paper is held on one side only and is allowed to freely hang unsupported toward the end of the paper.

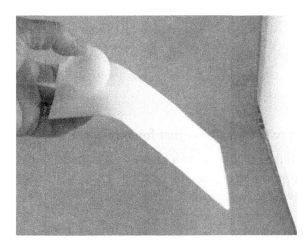

The bumps on the lotus leaf contain nano-scaled tubes oriented in random locations. This causes instability and, along with the weight of the water droplets, causes each droplet to roll along the leaf. This results in the water droplets falling off the lotus leaf similar to the ping-pong ball falling off our piece of paper.

**Questions:**

1. Would it make a difference if we used a different sized ball? Why or why not?

2. Is there any way we can prevent the ball from falling off the paper?

## Ray Comfort's — Just for Fun!

Tell a friend that you know a great trick. Put your hand palm down on the table and balance a full glass of liquid on the back of your hand. Bet your friend that they can't balance a glass on both hands at once (help your friend to put them in place).

## Applied Learning

The following activity or experiment illustrates important concepts for this portion of the coursework. Please make note of the scientific aspects of the activity as well as the specific areas of focus. These should reinforce important concepts and definitions that you have learned as you apply them.

## Science

Fluid dynamics

Newton's third law of motion

## Definition/Focus

The speed of air leaving a small hole will generate a force with an opposite, opposing force.

## Parts Lists

- Balloon (1)

- A friend to help you with the experiment

## Experiment

Have your friend stand three feet away from you and ask him/her to stand sideways and create a circle with his or her arms and hold that position (he or she should resemble the Letter "P").

Blow up the balloon but do not tie it. Once it is blown up, pinch the narrow (air-fill) end of the balloon between your fingers to prevent the air from leaving. Release the balloon and see if you can get it to pass through your friend's arms.

## ☑ Take Away

As air leaves the balloon, the force of the air causes the balloon to move in the opposite direction. The direction of the air-fill end of the balloon (where you inflate the balloon) determines the direction the balloon will travel. The erratic zigzag of the balloon is the result of the rapid expulsion of air through the narrow and flexible air-fill end. In contrast, if the air-fill end maintained a constant straight direction, the balloon would also follow a straight direction.

The propulsion system of the squid uses this same principle but is precise and efficient, unlike the erratic balloon. Understanding and harnessing what we can glean from the squid will contribute to nanobots with the ability to maneuver in difficult mediums such as the viscous fluids in the human body. This would revolutionize diagnosis of diseases with minimal invasion and pain.

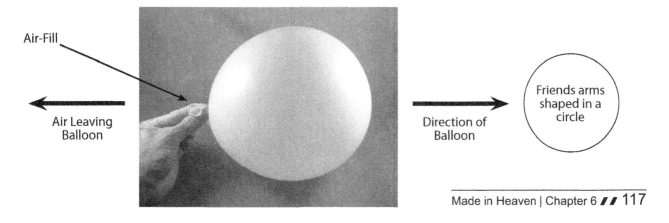

Air-Fill

Air Leaving Balloon

Direction of Balloon

Friends arms shaped in a circle

**Questions:**

1. Can you think of a way to regulate the direction of the balloon?

2. If we blew less air into the balloon, would the balloon go faster or slower when we release it?

3. What if you were to stand two feet away when releasing the balloon? How about a foot away? Note the results.

## Concepts and Definitions

The following information will lay a critical foundation for related Applied Learning activities. It is important that you read and understand this information so the Applied Learning opportunities can demonstrate and clarify important scientific concepts in action.

Understanding the properties of light waves in the natural world has contributed not only to visual technology but also some in areas that could affect our monetary system and national security. The basic properties of light waves can be broken down to a few basic properties that will help us expand our understanding of how God has used light waves in seemingly interesting areas in nature.

- Electromagnetic radiation
- Visible spectrum
- Wavelength
- Frequency
- Speed of light

## Electromagnetic Radiation

Light consists of both an electric field and a magnetic field traveling at right angles (90 degrees) to each other. Simultaneously they work together; it is teamwork at right angles in the direction of movement. They move together in perfect harmony to produce the light that we see with our eyes (see figure to the right).

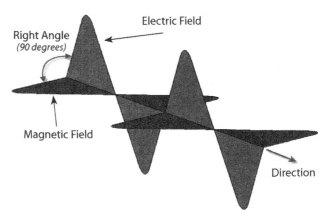

## Visible Spectrum

The electromagnetic spectrum is vast and consists of various types of rays. You may be surprised that the visible spectrum is the only portion that the human eyes can see and is, unfortunately, a small portion of the electromagnetic spectrum (see figure below). Note the sequence of colors that make up the visible spectrum.

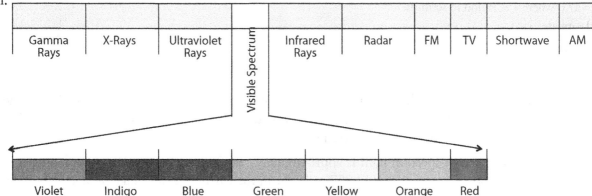

## Wavelength

Light travels in waves similar to the waves in an ocean with the exception that each color in the visible spectrum has its own wavelength.

Within the visible spectrum, each color has its own wavelength. The physical property of a wavelength is distinct to each color (i.e., 475 nm = blue). If the wavelength changes, so does the color.

All waves follow the same shape (just like sound waves as discussed in *Made in Heaven*). They take on the distinct sinusoidal shape (i.e., sine wave). The length of a wave is defined as the distance from one peak to the next (it can also be from one trough to the next). See below Figure: Wavelength, Definition.

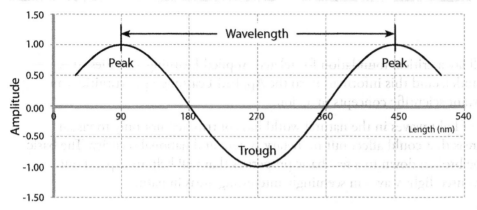

## Frequency

The unit of measurement for frequency is called Hertz, abbreviated as Hz. This is a measure of how many complete wavelengths are repeated in one second.

One cycle = one complete wavelength = 1 Hz

Each color is distinct from another *and* has its own wavelength and has its own frequency.

Distinct color = distinct wavelength = distinct frequency.

The figure to the right is an example of 2 Hz, where we have two complete wavelengths occurring during a one-second time period.

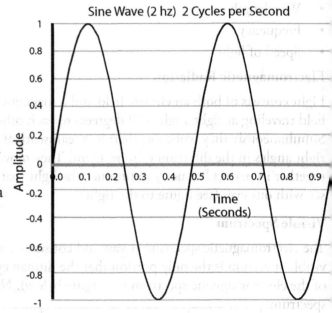

Recall: The sine wave or sinusoid in its most basic form is:

$y(t) = A * \sin(\omega + \Theta)$ (Equation 2) Where:

A = Amplitude
$\omega$ = Angular frequency/Circular frequency = $2\pi f$ (rad/s)
f = 1/T, where T = Period in seconds
$\Theta$ = phase
t = time(s)

## Speed of Light

No one can actually see the light moving across the room until it fills the room completely. It is not like filling a glass with water whereby we see the water moving from an empty glass to a full glass. What our eyes perceive is an instantaneous illumination of the room.

The reason for this is that speed of light is approximately 186,000 miles per second. To help put this in perspective, the moon is on average 238,857 miles from the earth. It would take light 1.3 seconds to travel from the moon to the earth.

### Summation of the Relationship between Wavelength, Frequency, and Speed of Light

All three parameters are inter-related with one other. Out of the three parameters, we know that the speed of light is constant, and both wavelength and frequency are variables. Therefore:

**Speed of Light = Wavelength x Frequency**

## Applied Learning

The following activity or experiment illustrates important concepts for this portion of the coursework. Please make note of the scientific aspects of the activity as well as the specific areas of focus. These should reinforce important concepts and definitions that you have learned as you apply them.

## Science

Light waves

## Definition/Focus

White light is made up of many colors

## Parts Lists

- Clear glass bowl
- Small mirror
- Water
- Flashlight
- A sheet of white paper

## Experiment

Place a small mirror inside the bowl of water. The mirror must be submerged in the water and sitting up on an angle. Hold a piece of white paper above the glass while shining a flashlight directly at the mirror. You will see the colors of the rainbow appear on the paper. You can try this experiment in a dark room to see the rainbow appear on the ceiling.

## ☑ Take Away

White light is made up of seven different color components. The color components are known by the acronym ROYGBIV = red, orange, yellow, green, blue, indigo, and violet.

The Mantis Shrimp can distinguish an astounding range of color, ten times that of humans. This could unlock a new world of color for the next wave of entertainment technology.

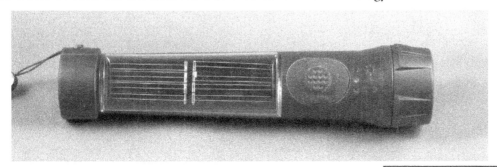

**Questions:**

1.  As you are conducting the experiment, list the colors that you see and the order in which they appear.




2.  What happens when you change the angle of the mirror? Or the angle of the flashlight?

| | | Butterflies Prevent Counterfeit Currency? | Day 126 | Chapter 8 Worksheet 1 | Name |
|---|---|---|---|---|---|
| | *Made in Heaven* | | | | |

## Applied Learning

The following activity or experiment illustrates important concepts for this portion of the coursework. Please make note of the scientific aspects of the activity as well as the specific areas of focus. These should reinforce important concepts and definitions that you have learned as you apply them.

## Science

Light waves

## Definition:

Light consists of wavelengths, which add or subtract from each other relative to their phase relationship.

## Discussion:

As discussed in the article "Butterflies Prevent Counterfeit Currency" in the book *Made In Heaven*, when light waves are in phase they are additive to each other. Light travels in a repetitive sinusoidal pattern, which has a distinct color and frequency. A sine wave is described as having both a peak and trough:

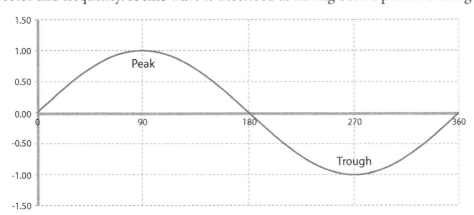

Sine waves of the same color come in contact with each other, thus beginning the phase relationship between both waves. The location of the peaks and troughs of each wave dictate these waves. Referencing the above figure, the peak occurs at 90 degrees and the trough occurs at 270 degrees. If another wave was to have the peak occur at 0 degrees and the trough occur at 180 degrees, then a comparison between both waves would result in them being out of phase by 90 degrees. This is the difference in angle between the peaks or the troughs (90 minus 0 = 90 or 270 minus 180 = 90, respectively):

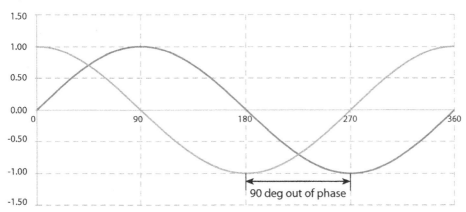

**Questions:**

1. How many degrees are in a sine wave?

2. What are two main features used to help describe a sine wave?

3. If two waves were 180 degrees out of phase with the same color intensity, what would the resultant wave look like?

**Ray Comfort's — Just for Fun!**

Ask someone for a U.S. dollar bill, and say, "See if you can find a camel on this side of the bill" (use the side with the graphic of a pyramid). As they begin to search for it, say, "It's a two-humped camel." Let them go for a few minutes until they talk about giving up. Then have them come really close to the picture on the bill, grab a pen or pencil to use as a pointer, and say, "There it is . . . just behind the pyramid!"

## Concepts and Definitions

The following information will lay a critical foundation for related Applied Learning activities. It is important that you read and understand this information so the Applied Learning opportunities can demonstrate and clarify important scientific concepts in action.

Optics is the branch of physics that deals with the behavior of light. Its properties outline how light interacts with different types of surfaces and the transmission of light through various mediums. In other words, how does light cooperate or change depending on what it hits and what happens to the light as it goes through different objects?

Optics defines for humans:

| | | |
|---|---|---|
| What we can see | > | Our parameters and limitations |
| How we see it | > | What happens to light when it hits a surface |
| What affects what we see | > | What if that surface is not solid but a liquid |
| Why we see what we see | > | What happens when it hits different types of surfaces |

We will discuss the basics of light since most of what the human eye perceives is subject to the light hitting various different mediums (surfaces). This will give a general framework on which to understand optics.

Let's first begin with a diagram explaining the components of light when it hits a surface. Light that travels toward a surface is defined as "the incident ray."

When the incident ray hits the surface it will do one of following:

1. It will be reflected > reflected ray
2. It will be absorbed > refracted ray
3. It will be both > reflected and refracted

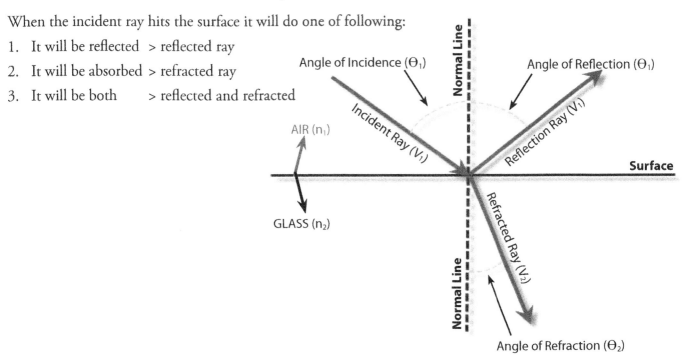

There is a relationship that is used to predict the outcome of an incident ray as it comes in contact with a surface. This relationship is called Snell's law.

**NOTE:** Snell's law is the expanded explanation found in *Made in Heaven* — #30 — Moth's Eye (refraction and reflection of light illustration). This is included for those who would like to further their study on the subject.

**Snell's Law**    $\sin\Theta_1/\sin\Theta_2 = v_1/v_2 = n_2/n_1$

Where,

$\Theta_1$ = angle of incidence

$\Theta_2$ = angle of refraction

$V_1$ = velocity of light in air

$V_2$ = velocity of light in glass

$n_1$ = index of refraction of air

$n_2$ = index of refraction of glass

## Index of Refraction (n)

The index of refraction is a ratio of the speed of light in a vacuum to the speed of light in the substance.

The index of refraction of air = 1.00 ($n_1$)

The index of refraction of glass = 1.52 ($n_2$)

## Applied Learning

The following activity or experiment illustrates important concepts for this portion of the coursework. Please make note of the scientific aspects of the activity as well as the specific areas of focus. These should reinforce important concepts and definitions that you have learned as you apply them.

## Science

Optics

## Definition/Focus

The wide field of view within the human vision system

## Parts Lists

- Camera
- Notepad (for notes)

## Experiment

1. Choose an interesting location such as a park or garden. Make sure to note where you are standing because you will need to be in this exact same spot for the second part of the experiment.

2. In this location, look straight ahead. Concentrate on everything that you can see in front of you. Make note how far to the left, right, top, and bottom you can see.

3. Return to the same location with your camera. Look in the same direction through the camera lens. Make note how far to the left, right, top and bottom you can see. Compare notes.

## ☑ Take Away

You will see much more in every direction with your eye than through a camera lens. The field of view in a camera is much smaller than the field of view of the human eye. The densities of our photoreceptors are far greater than any camera available on the market.

Engineers have come up with a clever solution of mimicking the curved surface sensor package with 256 photo detectors, but it still pales in comparison with the human eye's millions of photo detectors.

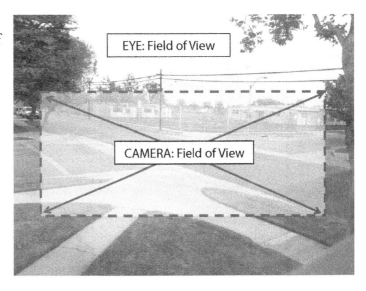

## Questions:

1. What difference did you note in how much you observed with your eye versus how much you observed when you looked through the camera?

2. Are you able to adjust the camera zoom lens to give you the same view as your eyes? Why or why not?

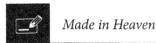
## Concepts and Definitions

The following information will lay a critical foundation for related Applied Learning activities. It is important that you read and understand this information so the Applied Learning opportunities can demonstrate and clarify important scientific concepts in action.

Mathematics is the science that assigns a numerical value to different variables to make sense of a problem. It is not random but ordered and follows set rules. Formulation of numeric values in the form of calculations can help solve a complex problem or move you closer to a solution.

God has created humans with cognitive skills. We see them in everyday things like analytical thinking — the ability to learn to communicate through language and written material and, of course, mathematical capabilities to solve problems.

Interestingly, God has internally put mathematical computations in some unexpected places. The examples in *Made in Heaven* delve into the calculations of combinations (No. 10) and how the relationship between the Fibonacci numbers and the golden angle align with one other (No. 32).

### Permutations

Permutations are a calculation of an ordered sequence. It is part of the mathematical analysis for probability estimates. This can help you determine your odds for success.

You can calculate permutations in two ways, dependent on the following:

> Repetition IS allowed      = maximum combinations
> Repetition is NOT allowed      = limited combinations

### 1) Repetition is allowed:

Combinations = $n^r$
where,

n   =   number of things to choose from

r   =   number of times to choose

For our example:

n   =   10 (numbers from 0 to 9)

r   =   3

**Combinations** = $10^3$ = 10 x 10 x 10 = **1,000**

### 2) Repetition is not allowed:

Combinations = $n!/(n-r)!$
where,

!   =   factorial function, means to multiply a series of descending natural numbers

n   =   number of things to choose from

r   =   number to times to choose

Example of ! (factorial function): 4! = 4 x 3 x 2 x 1 = 24

For our example:

n  =  10

r  =  3

**Combinations** = $\frac{10!}{(10-3)!}$ = $\frac{10!}{7!}$ = 10 x 9 x 8 = 720

**Repetition Allowed**

| 10 choices | 10 choices | 10 choices |

**1,000 Combinations**

**Repetition Not Allowed**

| 10 choices | 9 choices | 8 choices |

**720 Combinations**

## Applied Learning

The following activity or experiment illustrates important concepts for this portion of the coursework. Please make note of the scientific aspects of the activity as well as the specific areas of focus. These should reinforce important concepts and definitions that you have learned as you apply them.

## Science

Mathematical permutation

## Definition/Focus

Determination of number combinations

## Parts Lists

- Pencil
- Sheet of Paper

## Experiment

Create as many different combinations of a three-digit number as possible, using only the numbers 1, 2 and 3. Example 111, 321, 223, etc.

## ☑ Take Away

We can easily calculate the number of combinations by using the formula nr, where,

> n = number of digits, 3 (3-digit number)
>
> and
>
> r = number choices, 3 (we can chose between 1, 2 and 3).
>
> Number of combinations for these 3 numbers = 3 x 3 x 3 = 27.

It will be a difficult if not impossible task to model computer anti-virus software after the human immune system. Consider the following:

It takes 3,325,000,000,000 years to run the combination of a single peptide (which contains 20 amino acids). Now consider the 30,000 amino acids that are strung together and the staggering combinations to be computed in order to calculate the human immune system's antibodies (proteins) and you will see the mathematical odds of creating impervious anti-virus software.

Fill in the following table with all combinations:

| | | | | | | | |
|---|---|---|---|---|---|---|---|
| | | | | | | | |
| | | | | | | | |
| | | | | | | | |

**Questions:**

1. How many different combinations did you calculate for a three-digit number?

2. How long did it take you to come up with all 27 different combinations?

3. Calculate how many combinations there are for a four-digit number. Use the numbers from 1 to 4 with repetitions allowed.

4. How many computer viruses are found every day?

## Concepts and Definitions

The following information will lay a critical foundation for related Applied Learning activities. It is important that you read and understand this information so the Applied Learning opportunities can demonstrate and clarify important scientific concepts in action.

Our brain is the most complex organ in our body. It performs an astonishing amount of work on a daily basis to keep our body functioning. Interestingly, the brain occupies a small volume in proportion to its role and significance. The brain is made up of three main parts that share the workload:

- Cerebrum (fore brain — left and right hemisphere)
- Brainstem (mid brain)
- Cerebellum (hind brain)

## Cerebrum (Fore Brain)

Functions: Initiation of movement, coordination of movement, temperature, touch, vision, hearing, judgment, reasoning, problem solving, emotions and learning (to name a few things)

- Frontal Lobe — Control center of your brain, controls reasoning, problem solving, judgment, impulses, emotions, memory, personality characteristics, movement, and smell recognition
- Parietal Lobe — Identify objects, understand spatial relationships, interpreting pain and touch in the body
- Occipital Lobe — Involved with vision
- Temporal Lobe — Involved in memory, speech, musical rhythm, and some smell recognition

## Brainstem (Mid Brain)

Functions: Movement of the eyes and mouth, relaying sensory messages (hot, pain, loud, etc.), hunger, respirations, consciousness, cardiac function, body temperature, involuntary muscle movements, sneezing, coughing, vomiting, and swallowing.

- Pons — Controls eye and face movements
- Medulla — Controls breathing (lungs), heart rate, and digestion
- Spinal Cord — Main conduit to carry instructions from the brain to the rest of the body

## Cerebellum (Hind Brain)

Functions: Controls muscle movements, posture, balance, and equilibrium

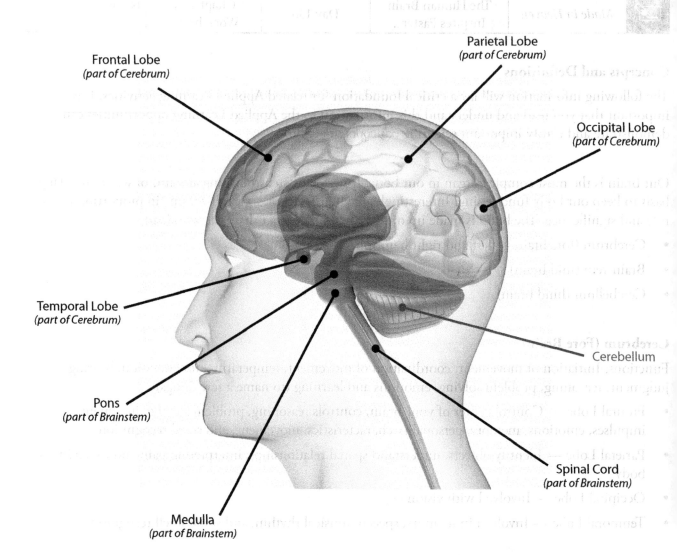

Frontal Lobe
*(part of Cerebrum)*

Parietal Lobe
*(part of Cerebrum)*

Occipital Lobe
*(part of Cerebrum)*

Temporal Lobe
*(part of Cerebrum)*

Cerebellum

Pons
*(part of Brainstem)*

Spinal Cord
*(part of Brainstem)*

Medulla
*(part of Brainstem)*

## Applied Learning

The following activity or experiment illustrates important concepts for this portion of the coursework. Please make note of the scientific aspects of the activity as well as the specific areas of focus. These should reinforce important concepts and definitions that you have learned as you apply them.

## Science

Brain anatomy

## Definition/Focus

Understanding the various functions of the brain

## Experiment

Step 1: Pick three tasks from the following list and perform them one at a time.

- Hop on one foot
- Spin in a circle
- Count backward from 20 to zero
- Raise one arm in the air
- Wink one eye rapidly

Step 2: Choose two tasks and perform (safely) simultaneously. Warning: Stop the tasks if you feel disoriented.

Step 3: Choose three tasks and perform (safely) simultaneously. Warning: Stop the tasks if you feel disoriented.

## ☑ Take Away

The ability to perform more than one task is not a simple matter. Contrast that to the human brain, which performs millions of tasks simultaneously.

Scientists are trying to understand and copy the human brain's ability to communicate through neurons. This is only one of many functions that the brain can perform. As you read what scientists are trying to replicate, meditate on Romans 11:33–34 and think about how the infinite genius of God is on display with every thought, word, and action.

**Questions:**

1. Were you able to perform three tasks simultaneously with the same ease as one task? Have you pondered how many tasks the brain controls simultaneously and the God who created the human brain?

2. Which task did you find the hardest to do?

3. Can you do four tasks simultaneously or perhaps the whole list?

4. If 42 semi-trailers represent the visual processing system (1/10th) of the brain, how many semi-trailers would you need to represent the whole brain?

**Ray Comfort's — Just for Fun!**

1. Say, "Imagine you are driving a Mercedes at 100 mph. The steering locks. The doors lock. The brakes fail. You can't get out. You are heading for a 1,000-foot cliff. What do you do?"

2. A rooster lays an egg at the very top of a slanted roof. Which side is the egg going to roll off on?

3. A man and his son had a terrible car accident and were rushed to the hospital. The man died on the way, but the son was still barely alive. When they arrived, an old gray surgeon was called in to operate. Upon seeing the young boy, the surgeon said, "I can't operate — this is my son." How is this possible?

4. How far can a dog run into the forest?

5. A plane crashed right on the border of the United States and Canada. Where do they bury the survivors?

6. Five pigeons are sitting on a fence. The farmer comes out and shoots one. How many are left?

7. Can you tie a knot in a piece of string without letting it go?

8. Ask "Is it possible to end a sentence with the word 'the'?"

9. A man on horseback went on a two-day trip. He left on Tuesday and arrived home on Tuesday. How could this be?

10. What is the opposite of not in?

11. Ask this question: "I have 20 sick sheep (say the "20 sick sheep" so that it sounds like "26 sheep") and one dies. I have 19 left. How could this be?

12. How can you make an egg stand on its end?

## Applied Learning

The following activity or experiment illustrates important concepts for this portion of the coursework. Please make note of the scientific aspects of the activity as well as the specific areas of focus. These should reinforce important concepts and definitions that you have learned as you apply them.

## Science

Wavelengths

## Definition/Focus

Every color in the spectrum has a physical length called a wavelength

## Discussion

All light travels in what is called a sine wave shape. All sine waves display a repetitive shape in which we can measure their length. This length (nanometers) is what we call a wavelength. It is measured from the peak of one wave to the peak of the other. Every color in the visible spectrum has its own wavelength associated with it (see below figure).

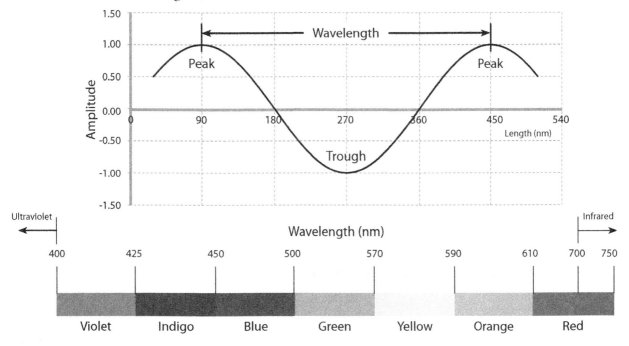

**Visible Light Spectrum**

## ☑ Take Away

The light that we can see with our eyes is called the "visible light spectrum," and it ranges from 400 nm to 700 nm. Any wavelengths that are below 400 nm are classified as ultraviolet (or UV) and any wavelengths above 700 nm are classified as infrared (or IR).

Scientists have discovered this as a "smart idea" and are starting to replicate the light spectrum by generating lasers away from the traditional method. They have come up with a mirror-less method of generating a laser in a thin sheet made of gallium arsenide. It has been coined the "anti-lasers." This is what they have learned from God's creation.

## Questions:

1. Approximately what wavelength would a blue jay bird have?

2. Which color has a shorter wavelength, red or green?

3. Name another example that God has created that has a wavelength.

## Concepts and Definitions

The following information will lay a critical foundation for related Applied Learning activities. It is important that you read and understand this information so the Applied Learning opportunities can demonstrate and clarify important scientific concepts in action.

The core of chemistry deals with the science behind the mixing of two or more substances together and observing the newly formed compound.

It begins with an understanding of the chemical structure of each individual substance, then a comparative chemical structure of the substances if they were to be combined.

There are two possible reactions as two or more substances merge.

a) Inhibit (neutral)     = there is NO chemical reaction: the result is a neutral reaction

b) Stimulate (initiate)  = there IS a chemical reaction initiated — these substances are reactants — a new compound has been formed.

For this study, we will be focusing on those substances that interact to initiate a new compound. These substances that stimulate (initiate) are also called reactants.

## Chemical Reactions

You might visually observe if a chemical reaction has occurred by watching the physical effects. You might observe a formation of a precipitate (a product, see below definition), color change, heat, light, gas emission, or a combination of different effects. The new substance will contain a different chemical identity from the original chemicals used; a chemical analysis will confirm a chemical reaction has taken place, as not all changes can be observed visually.

A true chemical reaction occurs when the following criteria occurs:

* Original bonds have been broken
* New bonds are formed
* Compounds disappear (reactants)
* New compounds are formed (products)

## Physical Process vs. Chemical Reaction

A chemical reaction is not simply when a substance changes its state from one form to another. Water as it freezes is not a chemical reaction. This is because there were no new chemical bonds formed nor broken as the water changed from a liquid to a solid.

**Conclusion:** Change of state from a solid, liquid, and gas are considered a physical process.

## Reactants

Reactants are the base chemicals present prior to any chemical reaction stimulation.

## Products

A product is what is formed after a chemical reaction has occurred. These are the chemicals present at the end of the reaction.

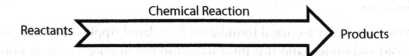

Reactants → Chemical Reaction → Products

## Applied Learning

The following activity or experiment illustrates important concepts for this portion of the coursework. Please make note of the scientific aspects of the activity as well as the specific areas of focus. These should reinforce important concepts and definitions that you have learned as you apply them.

## Science

Chemistry

Chemical reactions

## Definition/Focus

The process of different substances as they are mixed together, resulting in a noticeable fusion or reaction. The chemical reaction result is the formation of a product.

## Parts List:

- Cup or bowl
- 1 tsp. baking soda
- 3 tsp. vinegar

## Experiment:

In a cup or a bowl, place one teaspoon of baking soda. Then add three teaspoons of vinegar to the bowl of baking soda.

## ☑ Take Away

As separate components, the baking soda and vinegar are benign. This changes when they are combined. The end result is a visible chemical reaction.

Not all components are visibly reactant to one another. However, some like the bombardier beetle are the perfect example of different components exploding into a visible and dramatically observable chemical reaction.

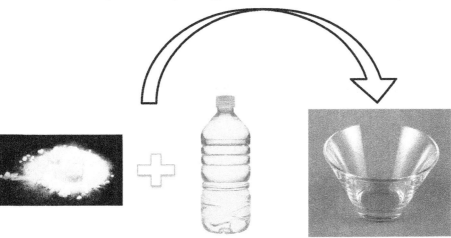

**Questions:**

1. What are the three reactants utilized by the bombardier beetle to ignite a chemical reaction?

2. What is the name of the product that is created after the chemical reaction has occurred?

3. What triggers the bombardier beetle to spray a caustic chemical projectile?

4. How many nozzles does the bombardier beetle employ to spray its caustic chemical projectile?

5. How far can the bombardier beetle spray?

6. How many pulses per second can the bombardier beetle fire off its toxic vapors?

7. What temperature does the benzoquinone reach before it is fired off?

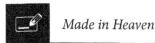
## Applied Learning

The following activity or experiment illustrates important concepts for this portion of the coursework. Please make note of the scientific aspects of the activity as well as the specific areas of focus. These should reinforce important concepts and definitions that you have learned as you apply them.

## Science

Mechanic of materials

Stress engineering

## Definition/Focus

Stress is the amount of pressure or load to which materials are subjected.

## Parts List:

- Modeling compounds such as clay or putty (2 large pieces, ½" thick x 4" diameter)
- Heavy book
- Drinking glass

## Experiment:

- Begin the experiment by placing the glass on top of one piece of modeling compound. Lay the book on top of the glass. You will notice that the glass will begin to sink into the modeling compound. Once the glass has settled and is stationary, remove the book and glass. Set this piece of modeling clay aside.

- Repeat the experiment with a slightly different twist. Place the glass upside down on the other piece of modeling compound with the book on top of the glass. Once the glass has settled and is stationary, remove the book and glass.

- Compare both impressions of the glass in the different pieces of modeling compound.

## ☑ Take Away

There is a direct correlation to the stress (PSI, pounds per square inch) in relationship to the depth of the impression that the glass imparts into the modeling compound.

Depth of the glass impression in the modeling compound = higher stress concentration.

Glass upright = The base of the glass comes in contact with the modeling compound
              (lower penetration, lower stress, higher contact area)

Glass upside-down = The rim of the glass comes in contact with the modeling compound
              (deeper penetration, higher stress, lower contact area).

The amount of stress that is produced by the glass onto the modeling compound can be calculated using the following formula:

$$\sigma = P/A$$

where,
$\sigma$ = Stress (psi, lbs/in$^2$), Greek letter sigma
P = Load (lbs) = weight of book
A = Area (in$^2$) = area of base / rim of glass

## Questions:

1. Compare the depth of penetration in the modeling compound between both the upright and upside down glass.

2. Calculate the stress if the book weighed 10 pounds and the area equaled 5 square inches.

3. What would the area be if the stress = 20 psi and the load = 40 pounds?

4. There is another factor that the mosquitos incorporate into their needles. What is it and why is it important?

### Ray Comfort's — Just for Fun!

Take a clean, crisp dollar bill and crease slightly, longwise in the middle. You are going to drop the bill toward the floor and you don't want it to be wind resistant, so it needs to be pulled straight and have a slight "V" so that it cuts through the air. Have someone open his or her thumb and forefinger in front of you. Hold the bill vertically between their thumb and forefinger with 90 percent of it below their hand. Tell them to catch it when you drop it.

## Concepts and Definitions

The following information will lay a critical foundation for related Applied Learning activities. It is important that you read and understand this information so the Applied Learning opportunities can demonstrate and clarify important scientific concepts in action.

Acoustics refers to the science (as defined by Merriam-Webster) that deals with the production, control, transmission, reception, and effects of sound. Acoustics deal with sound and sound waves.

One difficulty with understanding sound is that we cannot see it. We can, however, see the effects of sound and feel the propagation of sound waves, just as you feel the thumping vibration from a speaker when music is audibly loud. How do we visualize something we can't see? Studying the basic characteristics will help you grasp the understanding of both sound and acoustics.

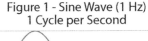

Figure 1 - Sine Wave (1 Hz)
1 Cycle per Second

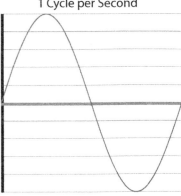

## Shape

Did you know that there is a shape to sound? That shape looks something like this: Sound travels along in waves, just like the waves in the ocean. There are peaks (highs) and troughs (lows) that form the shape of sound. These determine the intensity (loudness) level. Higher peaks and lower troughs of the wave equal louder sound.

The shape of sound can be visualized like the waves of the ocean: the higher the waves, the bigger the swells. This shape is what is commonly referred to as a sinusoidal shape, or a sine wave. It is a repetitive shape that follows the same pattern, where one complete cycle consists of one peak and one trough.

Figure 2 - Sine Wave (2 Hz)
2 Cycles per Second

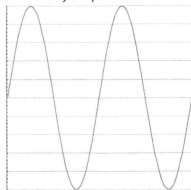

## Frequency

Our ears pick up sound vibrations, which transmit as a low, deep sound or a high pitched squealing sound. That is to say that our ears can distinguish between the range of sound and pitches.

Sound possesses frequency. We can hear sound according to a range of frequencies. In humans, that ranges in frequency from roughly 20 Hz to 20,000 Hz.

### Hz = Hertz = Cycles per Second.

What is a hertz? It is the complete cycle of a sine wave (one peak and one trough) repeated per second. Count the sine waves per second and you have your frequency. For example, if in one second we count two complete sine waves, then we know that the frequency would be 2 Hz or 2 cycles per second.

An example of a 5 Hz sine wave is on the right.

Figure 3 - Sine Wave (5 Hz)
5 Cycles per Second

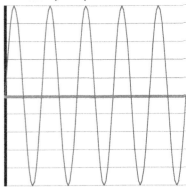

There is a distinct sound we hear in each frequency. We hear low bass-laden sounds in lower frequencies. Conversely, higher frequencies resonate like high-pitched squeals that can irritate our ears. Everyday noises generate a different sound to our ears, from the low rumbling of a train to the high-pitched squealing of tires.

We hear different frequencies in music, with some vocalists singing in a dulcet deep melody compared to opera singers that sing high notes that sound almost piercingly painful to our ears.

Frequency is easily seen in relation to musical notes. Musical notes are assigned letters with a unique frequency. What does sound look like?

Let's take a look at someone who plays the first octave note G on the chart below. They are playing a note that has a frequency of 49 Hz.

| Musical Note | Octave | Frequency (Hz) |
|---|---|---|
| C | 0 | 16.35 |
| D | 0 | 18.35 |
| E | 0 | 20.60 |
| F | 0 | 21.83 |
| G | 0 | 24.50 |
| A | 0 | 27.50 |
| B | 0 | 30.87 |

| Musical Note | Octave | Frequency (Hz) |
|---|---|---|
| C | 1 | 32.70 |
| D | 1 | 36.71 |
| E | 1 | 41.20 |
| F | 1 | 43.65 |
| G | 1 | 49.00 |
| A | 1 | 55.00 |
| B | 1 | 61.74 |

### Intensity

Intensity of sound is measured based on a ratio between a measured and referenced power level. This unit of measurement is called a decibel (dB). Please note that the dB scale is not a linear scale. It follows a logarithmic (or exponential) scale.

Listed below are common sounds and their dB value so that we might get a better understanding of sound levels on a decibel scale.

| | |
|---|---|
| Whisper: | 30 dB |
| Normal Conversation: | 60–65 dB |
| Piano: | 60–70 dB |
| Violin: | 82–92 dB |
| Jet engine (@ 100 ft.): | 140 dB |

(Source: http://www.gcaudio.com/resources/howtos/loudness.html)

### Acoustics — Summary

In summary, as we hear sound, we can characterize it by the following:

1. Frequency
2. Intensity

The tone and loudness of sounds that we hear can be described by stating both the frequency and intensity:

Example: 2000 Hz @ 60 dB.

This means that we are hearing a sound at a frequency of 2000 Hz with an intensity level of 60 db.

---

## Applied Learning

The following activity or experiment illustrates important concepts for this portion of the coursework. Please make note of the scientific aspects of the activity as well as the specific areas of focus. These should reinforce important concepts and definitions that you have learned as you apply them.

## Science

Sound waves

## Definition/Focus

Sound travels through the air. Although we cannot see sound waves we can see the effects.

## Parts List:

- Bowl (medium size)
- Grains of uncooked rice (approx. 20)
- Plastic wrap
- Cookie sheet or baking tray

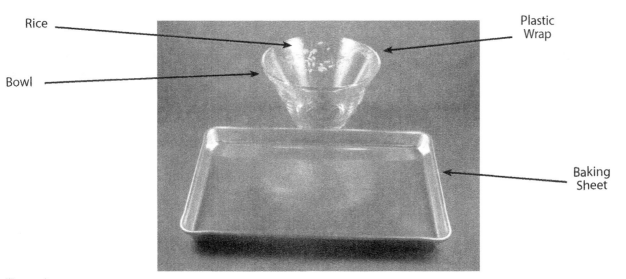

## Experiment:

Tightly stretch a piece of plastic wrap over the top of the bowl, securing the sides for a flat fit. Lay around 20 grains of uncooked rice on top of the plastic wrap. Hold a cookie or baking sheet a few inches above the bowl (do not touch the bowl) then hit the sheet to create a loud banging sound.

## ☑ Take Away

The plastic wrap represents the diaphragm in our eardrum. The sound that the cookie or baking sheet made traveled in the air and hit the plastic wrap. The plastic wrap deflected due to the sound waves and caused the grains of rice to move.

The science of sound waves begins to explain why sound is so intricate. The Ormia ochracea fly is configured for hearing precision, which explains why someone would patent a fly's hearing system. The patent on their ears is a patent on their incredible sound system.

**Questions:**

1. What would be the result of the grains of rice in our experiment (in terms of deflection) if we increase the intensity (loudness) of the sound?

2. Do you think that the rice would move if you punctured the plastic wrap? Try this and document the results.

3. Do you think it would it make a difference if the sound came from another side of the bowl?

4. Read the article "Listen Like a Fly on a Wall" in the book *Made in Heaven*. The ears of an *Ormia ochracea* fly pinpoints sounds immediately. How are their ears different from human ears? What allows the precision in their hearing system?

5. What is the frequency for the 3rd octave for the musical note G?

6. How many peaks and troughs would there be for a frequency of 2 Hz over a time of 3 seconds?

## Applied Learning

The following activity or experiment illustrates important concepts for this portion of the coursework. Please make note of the scientific aspects of the activity as well as the specific areas of focus. These should reinforce important concepts and definitions that you have learned as you apply them.

## Science

Fluid dynamics

## Definition/Focus

Fluid flow of different objects

## Parts List:

- Quarter
- Dime
- Frozen peas
- Tall clear glass
- Water

## Experiment:

Fill a glass with water and leave a little space on top, being careful not to overfill. Drop the quarter, dime, and a frozen pea in the glass one at a time. Observe the rate of speed of each object as it drops to the bottom of the glass.

## ☑ Take Away

The mass of a solid object plays a part on its behavior within a liquid component. That is why heavier objects move faster and lighter objects move slower.

As we see in our experiment, a mixture of both heavy and lighter objects descending simultaneously down the same path will result in the lighter objects being pushed outward.

This is exactly what happens with the blood platelets in our body. They are pushed to the walls of the blood vessels as blood flows. Platelets are lightest and therefore they get there first. This allows them to clump not only to each other but also to the break in the blood vessel, which speeds up healing.

**Questions:**

1. Which object was the slowest in descending to the bottom of the glass? Why?

2. Which object was the fastest to reach the bottom of the glass? Why?

3. Which object represents the platelets? Why?

4. Repeat the experiment but drop all items simultaneously. Were the results the same?

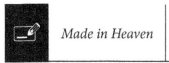
## Applied Learning

The following activity or experiment illustrates important concepts for this portion of the coursework. Please make note of the scientific aspects of the activity as well as the specific areas of focus. These should reinforce important concepts and definitions that you have learned as you apply them.

## Science

Mechanics of materials

## Definition/Focus

Pressure

Our fingertips can sense different materials based on touch only.

It can adjust pressure required to pick up an object accordingly.

## Parts List:

- Small piece of tissue
- Copper penny
- Popsicle stick
- Rubber eraser

- Plastic straw
- Blindfold (or something to cover your eyes)
- A friend to help with the experiment (do NOT let them see the objects listed above)

## Experiment:

Place a blindfold on a friend. Ask them to hold out one hand and place the other hand behind their back. Hand them an object from the list above, one at a time in the open palm of their hand. Ask them to identify the material of each object (i.e., paper, metal, cotton, rubber, plastic). They may not use their fingertips or any other sense to identify the item, just the palm of their hand. Repeat the experiment, but this time allow them to use their fingertips to help identify the materials.

☑ **Take Away**

The sensitivity of our fingertips is incredible. As we adjust the amount of pressure we apply to an object (i.e., light or firm pressure) we are able to determine the amount of pressure required to grasp or pick up an object by the added sensitivity of our fingertips.

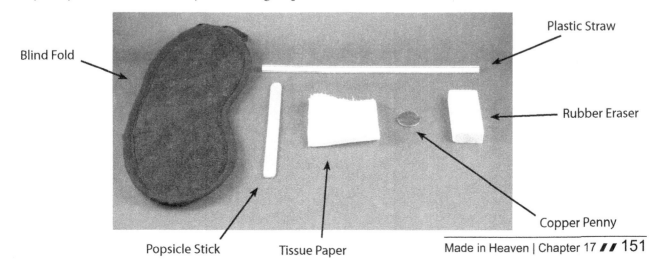

Blind Fold — Plastic Straw — Rubber Eraser — Copper Penny — Popsicle Stick — Tissue Paper

**Questions:**

1. What other objects could you use to test your sense of touch?

2. Do you think the back of your hand has the same sensitivity as your fingertips?

3. If you were to touch the objects with only a single finger or a thumb, would you get the same result?

**Ray Comfort's — Just for Fun!**

Here's a great experiment to show human predictability. Take two pennies or two quarters. Hide one in the palm of your left hand. Take a cup and put it on a table. Put the other coin on the table beside it. Then boldly say, "I am going to get this coin without touching the cup." As you say that, place the cup over the coin. Then, without revealing the coin in your left hand (using a little drama) hit the underside of the table under the cup. Then open your hand and say, "There you are! Got it!"

Ask a group of people if they like magic. Get a china cup and a saucer and ask them if they think that you can push the saucer through the handle of the cup. When they say that they think you can't do it, dramatically make room on the table, look closely at the cup and ask if it's expensive (pretending that you may break it), and then ask those who are standing close to move back in case it doesn't work. Then place the saucer on the table, poke your forefinger through the handle of the cup, and push the saucer across the table. You are pushing the saucer through the handle of the cup.

Take any size piece of paper and say, "I don't think you can fold this piece of paper in half (it must be folded in half) more than eight times."

Where can you put your right hand where your left hand can't touch it?

## Applied Learning

The following activity or experiment illustrates important concepts for this portion of the coursework. Please make note of the scientific aspects of the activity as well as the specific areas of focus. These should reinforce important concepts and definitions that you have learned as you apply them.

## Science

Mechanics of materials

## Definition/Focus

Contact strength

Bonding strength of different objects composed of different materials

## Parts List:

- Suction cup with hook
- Small plastic bag filled with a dozen small coins

## Experiment:

Pierce a small hole in your small bag of coins. Feed the hook through the small plastic bag. Begin to attach the bag and suction cup to the following surfaces and note the adhering strength of each:

- Plaster (wall)
- Glass (window)
- Wood (shelf)
- Refrigerator door (metal door)
- Plastic (table)

Small Hole In Bag

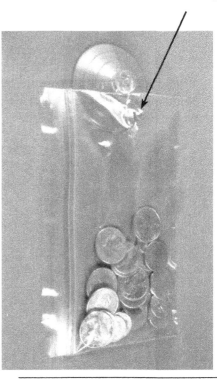

## ☑ Take Away

We're using the suction cup to represent the mussel's foot and byssal threads. The bag of coins represents the pounding of the waves trying to dislodge the mussel from its foothold. The mussel has the capability of attaching itself to any type of surface — incredible, since it begins the process while it is under water. Adhesives are a billion-dollar industry. There isn't anything to date that rivals the adhesive properties of the mussel.

**Questions:**

1. Did you have difficulty adhering the suction cup to any of the surfaces? List the surface(s).

2. Did you require moistening for adherence of the suction cup to the surface?

3. What types of industry would be revolutionized if scientists could replicate the mussel's sticking power? Name some of the areas that would be affected and some of the applications.

## Research Paper:

Now that you have finished reading *Men of Science, Men of God* , it is time to pick out one or more scientists as the subject(s) of a research paper. Here are some initial tips and structure for this project:

## Hint!

A rough outline can be very helping in organizing your thoughts and research before you actually begin the work of writing.

## General Tips:

* Whether your paper is hand-written or typed, it is important for it to be neat and organized.

* It is better to use more than one source for your paper. You should already be using *Men of Science, Men of God* as a source. Visit the library to find out more about your scientist and choose an additional book or two for your source work. Or visit Google books or Project Gutenberg online to find free e-books that you can use.

## Your Assignment:

* Select a scientist from the book *Men of Science, Men of God* and write a two-page biographical paper. Include descriptions of key discoveries as well as relevant or interesting biographical history and details.

## Structure of Paper:

* Introduction:

   Make sure your introduction includes a topic sentence – what/who this paper is about and what main points you will be covering, or at least a general topic on which your paper will be focused.

* Body:

   This is where you present your main points. While it is not a set rule, it is always a good idea to have at least three main points that support, explain, or add details related to your topic sentence.

* Conclusion:

   You should have presented a well-reasoned and well-written set of main points in the body. The conclusion is where you:

   Remind the reader of the focus of your paper, have one or two sentences that encompass the main points you have made to support the focus of the paper.

   A sentence or two that answers one of the following questions:

   ◊ What did you find the most interesting about this scientist and his life?

   ◊ How did his faith or his life history influence the discoveries that he made?

   ◊ Is the scientist's work still relevant or used today in some way?

There will be one more point in this course (page 168 of this Teacher Guide) where you will be reminded of this assignment and given tips on how to begin, if for some reason you haven't started the research paper by that point. Please keep in mind that it takes time and effort to create a well-researched and well-written paper.

## Research Paper

Now that you have finished reading *Men of Science, Men of God*, it is time to pick out one or more scientists as the subject(s) of a research paper. Here are some start-up tips for this semester.

### Hint

A rough outline can be very helpful in organizing your thoughts and ideas before you actually begin the work of writing.

### General Tips

- Whether your paper is hand-written or typed, it is important for it to be neat and organized.
- It is better to use more than one source for your paper. You should already be using *Men of God* as a source. Visit the library to find out more about your scientist and choose an additional book or two for your source work. Or visit Google books or Project Gutenberg online to find free e-books that you can use.

### Your Assignment

- Select a scientist from the book *Men of Science, Men of God* and write a two page (minimum) paper.
- Include descriptions of key discoveries as well as what is interesting or important in personal history and details.

### Structure of Paper

- Introduction

  Make sure your introduction includes a topic sentence — what focus this paper is about and what main points you will be covering, or at least a general idea on which your paper will be focused.

- Body

  This is where you present your main points. While there is no set rule, it is always a good idea to have at least three main points that support, explain, or add detail related to your topic sentence.

- Conclusion

  You should have presented a well researched and well written set of main points in the body. The conclusion is where you

  Remind the reader of the focus of your paper. Have one or two sentences that summarize the main points you have made to support the focus in the paper.

  A sentence or two that answers one of the following questions:

  ◊ What did you find the most interesting about this scientist and his life?

  ◊ How did his faith or his life history influence the discoveries that he made?

  ◊ Is the scientist's work still relevant or used today in some way?

There will be one more point in this course (Day 198 of the Teacher Guide) where you will be reminded of this assignment and given tips on how to begin. It does take some reason you haven't started the research by that point. Please keep in mind that it takes time and effort to create a well-researched and well-written paper.

## Applied Learning

The following activity or experiment illustrates important concepts for this portion of the coursework. Please make note of the scientific aspects of the activity as well as the specific areas of focus. These should reinforce important concepts and definitions that you have learned as you apply them.

### Science

Mechanics of materials

### Definition/Focus

Load distribution

More attachments = easier lifting of a load

### Parts List:

- Medium-sized hardcover book
- String or twine
- Cardboard box (disassembled)
- Clothesline
- Clothespins
- Pencil

### Experiment:

1. Place a book in the middle of your cardboard piece. Using your pencil, trace your book to make a template and cut out this piece. Pierce a hole in the center of the template, about 2" from the bottom edge (lengthwise).

2. Open your book in half. While open, wrap your string around the book, leaving enough string to form a "handle" (similar to a purse handle).

3. Thread the string through the cardboard template hole and knot it up so that it will not slip through your cardboard. Your book is now hanging from the piece of cardboard on a string and should resemble a purse.

4. Take the book-on-cardboard to the clothesline. Begin attaching clothespins until the book stays suspended on the clothesline.

### ☑ Take Away

More clothespins = more load distribution = book stays suspended in air

Velcro uses a nylon hook-and-loop combination to distribute the load. The result has been so successful that NASA has utilized Velcro on space shuttle missions.

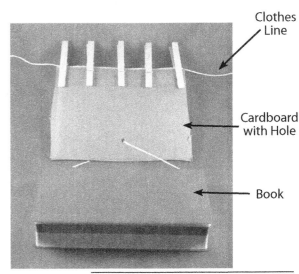

Clothes Line

Cardboard with Hole

Book

**Questions:**

1. How many clothespins were required to support the book? What is the weight of the book?

2. Determine the load per clothespin with the following equation. Divide the weight of the book by the number of clothespins used. What is the load per clothespin?

3. Calculate the load per clothespin if you were to use four additional clothespins.

4. Name other materials besides nylon that are being used to fabricate Velcro. Where could these be used?

## Applied Learning

The following activity or experiment illustrates important concepts for this portion of the coursework. Please make note of the scientific aspects of the activity as well as the specific areas of focus. These should reinforce important concepts and definitions that you have learned as you apply them.

## Science

Structural adhesion

## Definition/Focus

Adhesives used to bond surfaces together

## Parts List:

- Newspaper (cut into strips 1" wide x 4" long)
- Balloon
- White flour (½ cup)
- Water (⅔ cup)
- Safety pin

## Experiment:

Fill a small balloon with air; approximately six to eight inches in diameter. Mix ½ cup of white flour and ⅔ cup of water in a mixing bowl. Stir until the mixture is a paste-like texture.

Saturate one strip of newspaper in the paste mixture and apply to the balloon. Repeat until the balloon is completely covered. Make sure balloon is smooth and free of excess paste. Allow your newspaper-covered balloon to dry, approximately 24 to 48 hours.

Insert the safety pin. The balloon should pop but the dried newspaper shaped to the balloon will remain.

## ☑ Take Away

Adhesives come in many forms and can be used to bond various materials together. Our experiment bonded paper together to form a round shape. The wasp's saliva contains proteins, which help bond the wood fibers together to make their nest. Once dry, the shape remains.

**Questions:**

1. What other objects can you use instead of a balloon as your interior shape? What external materials other than newspaper could you substitute as your exterior mold?

2. Compare modern papermaking to wasp papermaking. Which is superior and why?

3. Gutenberg was named one of the most influential people in history. He invented the printing press, which opened information to the masses, beginning with the Bible. How have books impacted your life?

**Just for Fun:**

1. Say, "I bet you can't write this sentence down and be speaking the truth."

2. Say, "I want you to write something on a piece of paper. Write a small 'I' with a dot on the top."

3. Rearrange the letters in the words "new door" to make one word.

4. What word can be written forward, backward, or upside-down while still retaining the same word?

## Applied Learning

The following activity or experiment illustrates important concepts for this portion of the coursework. Please make note of the scientific aspects of the activity as well as the specific areas of focus. These should reinforce important concepts and definitions that you have learned as you apply them.

## Science

Optics

## Definition/Focus

Reflection of light

## Parts List:

- Small round bowl
- Foil wrap
- Flashlight

## Experiment:

Line the inside of the bowl with some foil wrap (shiny side up). Mold the tin foil to the bowl, keeping it as smooth as possible. Fold all excess foil around the edge of the bowl. Standing a foot away from the bowl, aim the flashlight at the center of the bowl.

## ☑ Take Away

As the light hits the foil, it reflects back toward you because of the curved surface. The curved surface causes the light to reflect back the same way it came in. This is referred to as retroreflection. The reflective pigment layer of a cat's eyes lend to their shining appearance when they are illuminated in the dark as are their namesake, "Cats eye" road reflectors.

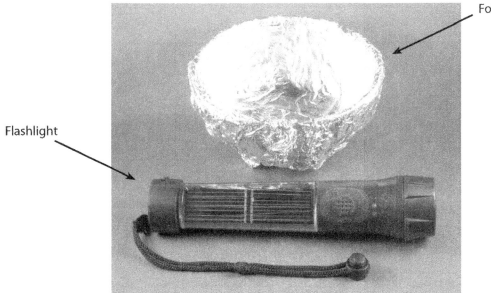

Foil Wrap Lined Bowl

Flashlight

**Questions:**

1. What happens if you aim the light at a different angle during the experiment?

2. What happens if you move the light farther from the bowl?

3. Would any other shape that is not curved still work?

## Concepts and Definitions

The following information will lay a critical foundation for related Applied Learning activities. It is important that you read and understand this information so the Applied Learning opportunities can demonstrate and clarify important scientific concepts in action.

Electromagnetism is the unified relationship between electricity and magnetism. It was a distinct phenomenon until the 19th century and represents a key development for modern physics.

## Electricity

The flow of electrons (current) through a conductor (metal) such as a wire as they move from one place to another (see figure below).

## Magnetic field

A force that is defined as having both a north and south pole. Particles follow a set pattern moving between poles.

## Electromagnetism

Electromagnetism = electricity + magnetic field. A magnetic field will only exist if there is electricity flowing. No electricity = no magnetic field.

## What does this mean?

Since electromagnetism is the creation of a magnetic field when there is an electric current, we can create magnets by running electricity through wires wrapped around metal. Iron is an excellent conductor and the metal of popular choice for the magnets we use today.

A magnetic field is not random but something we can control. Using a switch we can turn the flow of electricity on or off.

**Switch On** = The flow of electricity begins and the magnetic field is created.

**Switch Off** = The flow of electricity stops and the magnetic field diminishes.

## What does a controlled magnetic field look like?

Great visuals of electromagnetism are the large cranes used in junkyards to pick up wrecked metal cars. The operator can flip a switch to turn on and off the magnetic field so that they can move the cars from one location to another.

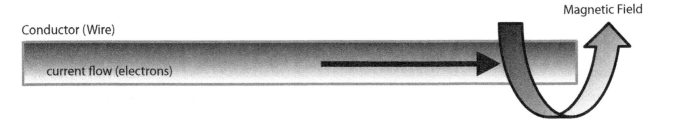

Conductor (Wire)

current flow (electrons)

Magnetic Field

## Electrostatic Forces:

The magnetic field is composed of particles and held together with electrostatic forces. Electrostatic forces are identified as either a proton or an electron — depending on their polarity. Please also refer to the visual chart below:

Protons (+) = positive polarity

Electrons (-) = negative polarity

## Rules for Polarity:

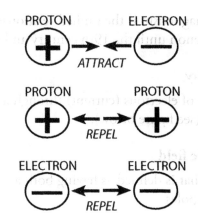

> Opposite polarities <u>attract</u>

   Proton (positive) attracts electron (negative)

   Result: a pulling or drawing toward each other

> Similar polarities <u>repel</u>

   Proton repels proton (positive repels a positive)

   Electron repels electron (negative repels a negative)

   Result: A moving or pushing away from one another

A further look at a magnetic field will show particles having opposite polarities joining together to make up the magnetic field (see figure below).

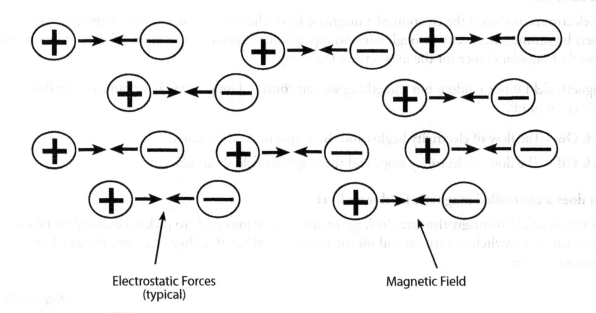

Electrostatic Forces
(typical)

Magnetic Field

## Conclusion:

Understanding the principles of opposite polarities being attracted to each other helps us to grasp the science of electromagnetism and electrostatic forces, since we can only see the effects of the force and not the force itself.

## Applied Learning

The following activity or experiment illustrates important concepts for this portion of the coursework. Please make note of the scientific aspects of the activity as well as the specific areas of focus. These should reinforce important concepts and definitions that you have learned as you apply them.

## Science

Electromagnetism

Electrostatic

## Definition

Attraction of positive and negative forces

## Parts List:

- Plastic comb

- Sink

## Experiment:

The results are best seen if you have someone with medium to long hair assisting you with this experiment.

Begin by turning on the faucet and running the water at a slow rate. Stand near the sink and run the comb through the hair at least 10 to 15 times.

Slowly bring the comb to the water, but do not touch the water. You will notice the flow of water bending toward the comb.

## ☑ Take Away

You are negatively charging the comb by adding electrons to the comb from your hair (after repeated brushing). Rubbing these two surfaces together generates friction. As you bring the comb closer to the water, the opposite charges between the comb (negative) and the water (positive) attract each other, pulling (drawn) to each other.

The gecko's toes have setae (hairs). These setae in turn branch off into hundreds of tips called spatula. Although small, these spatulas number in the millions and they produce enough positive and negative forces to stick to almost any surface. Stickybot was inspired by the gecko's "sticky" toes and could change the robot landscape.

**Questions:**

1.  What is the scientific term for the small forces that the gecko's spatula generates?

2.  Can you think of another experiment safely demonstrating electromagnetism?

## Concepts and Definitions

The following information will lay a critical foundation for related Applied Learning activities. It is important that you read and understand this information so the Applied Learning opportunities can demonstrate and clarify important scientific concepts in action.

## Review

Review the information on page 103 of this Teacher Guide, regarding the science of fluid dynamics. Many of these principles will apply to this example from *Made in Heaven*. Make sure you are familiar with these aspects of this study:

* Boundary Layer

* Laminar Flow

* Turbulent Flow

* Transition Point

* Streamlines

* Drag

**Invention Notebook** (pg. 101 of this Teacher Guide):

Make sure your invention notebook is progressing. It is important to be both practical but also very creative in how to you document and present your ideas at the completion of this course.

You can use a variety of things to help visually convey your ideas, including sketches, cutouts, and more to be utilized in numerous ways if you wish.

While the project notebook is a collection of your thoughts, testing, and imagination regarding a possibly invention inspired by nature, it is still important to be able to articulate your idea. Please write a one-page presentation of your project with a potential investor or interested group in mind. Cover at least two or more of the following topics:

* Why your invention is needed?

* Does it create a solution to an existing problem or would it be an idea to make life better or easier?

* How it could be created or marketed?

* How is the group most likely to be interested in your idea (military, retail, cosmetic companies, construction, etc)?

* Note any potential cost factors (using recycled materials is one way costs can be minimized).

* Will it have a positive or negative environmental impact?

* How did your faith enable you to appreciate the beauty and inventive aspects of nature?

**Research Paper** (review pg. 5 of this Teacher Guide):

You need to begin making some decisions on your research paper on a scientist if you haven't already. Some of the following points may be of assistance to you in your efforts:

Which scientist or discovery to focus on:

- What are the main points of your paper?
- What ideas/inventions did they contribute to scientific knowledge?
- Does their work still have a lasting impact today?
- Did they benefit from their ideas?
- Is their work the foundation of other ideas or inventions?

What sources of information you will use.

How you will document your sources.

## Concepts and Definitions

The following information will lay a critical foundation for related Applied Learning activities. It is important that you read and understand this information so the Applied Learning opportunities can demonstrate and clarify important scientific concepts in action.

## Conservation of Mass Flow

This is an underlying principle we must consider in relation to the flow of fluids within any duct (conduit).

The mass flow of the fluid will be identical at the inlet (front), throat (middle), and outlet (back).

Location doesn't matter along the length of the duct; the mass flow value will be identical throughout.

To help explain this concept, here is an example of the use of the mass flow equation in satisfying the conservation of mass.

## How to Use the Conservation of Mass Equation

## Example:

Water is flowing in the Venturi duct at 6 ft/sec, the cross-sectional areas of both the inlet and the outlet are 3 ft². The cross-sectional area of the throat is 1 ft². What is velocity of the water at the throat?

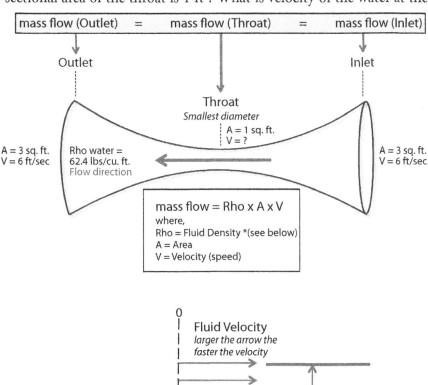

* The fluid density of any fluid is the measure of the weight per cubic volume.

Example:   What is the weight of a cubic foot of water (i.e., 1 ft x 1 ft x 1 ft)?

Answer:      62.4 pounds

**Solution:**

Using the mass flow equation: mass flow = Rho x A x V, we know the area and velocity of the inlet, and we also now the density of water. Therefore we can calculate the mass flow of the water at the inlet:

$A_{Inlet}$      = 3 ft²

$V_{Inlet}$      = 6 ft/sec

$Rho_{water}$ = 62.4 lbs/ft³

Mass Flow (Inlet) = Rho x A x V = 62.4 x 3 x 6 = 1123.2 lbs/sec

The conservation of mass flow needs to be satisfied, therefore:

Mass flow (Inlet) = mass flow (throat) = 1123.2 lbs/sec (pounds per second)

Therefore,

$Rho_{water}$ (density) x $A_{Throat}$ (area) x $V_{Throat}$ (velocity) = 1123.2 lbs/sec

But we are given: AThroat = 1 ft², and Rhowater = 62.4 lbs/ft³

Substituting above values we end up with,

62.4 x 1 x $V_{Throat}$ = 1123.2

Rearranging the equation and solving for $V_{Throat}$, gives us:

$V_{Throat}$ = 1123.2 / (62.4 x 1) = 18 ft/sec

☑   And the answer is: The velocity of water at the inlet equal to 6 ft/sec, the corresponding velocity at the throat will be 18 ft/sec.

## Applied Learning

The following activity or experiment illustrates important concepts for this portion of the coursework. Please make note of the scientific aspects of the activity as well as the specific areas of focus. These should reinforce important concepts and definitions that you have learned as you apply them.

## Science

Fluid dynamics

Conservation of mass flow

## Definition

The amount of fluid going in must equal the same amount of fluid going out. Simply put, what comes in must come out.

## Parts List:

- Plastic 2-liter soda pop bottle with cap
- Scissors
- Water
- Sink
- Nail and hammer (adult supervision required)
- Piece of wood
- Sandpaper (optional)
- Tape (optional)

## Experiment:

Using a pair of scissors, carefully cut off the bottom of your plastic bottle. Discard this small section.

**Caution:** Be careful with this newly cut section, as there may be sharp edges. You may want to use sandpaper to smooth out any sharp or rough edges. Alternatively, you can place tape where you cut the bottle to create a smooth edge.

Remove the cap from this section and place flat side down on a piece of wood. Carefully use a nail and hammer to tap a small hole in the cap (adult supervision required). Ensure there are no sharp edges or use a small piece of sandpaper to smooth your new small hole. Place the cap back on the bottle, ensuring that it is twisted closed.

Standing at your sink, hold the bottle upside down, with the cap facing the bottom of the sink. Lightly use your thumb to cover the small hammer hole and begin slowly filling the bottle with water while holding the bottle with your other hand.

Once the bottle is ¾ full, turn off the faucet. Remove your thumb from the cap hole and let the water flow through your newly made small nail hole. Observe the rate of flow of the water of both the top and bottom.

☑ **Take Away**

Observe that the water at the top (the large end of the bottle) appears to be moving downward slowly yet the water exiting the small end appears to be moving at a faster rate. The amount of fluid on the large end of the bottle that is flowing down must equal the same amount of fluid flowing out of the small end, which is why you see the fluid moving faster. This is the conservation of mass flow.

The same holds true for the termite mounds in the Zimbabwean Savannah that cool down naturally because their mounds are built with airflow in mind. The shape of their tunnels are tapered and have inlets (bottom) and outlets (top) and what is accomplished is the conservation of mass flow as faster-moving air creates a cooling effect. This was observed and copied at Eastgate Mall in Zimbabwe. It is an incredible example of architectural bionics.

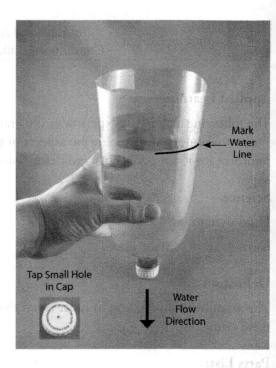

**Questions:**

1. Would the water move faster or slower if we made the hole larger in the cap?

2. Conversely, if the hole in the cap were smaller, would the fluid move faster or slower?

3. The termite mounds do not need any help to achieve conservation of mass flow. However, the Eastgate Mall needs a little help in this area. What does the mall require to keep the air flowing so that the air does not stay stagnant and warm?

| | *Made in Heaven* | Broken Bones, Healing, and the Eiffel Tower | Day 167 | Chapter 26 Worksheet 1 | Name |
|---|---|---|---|---|---|

## Applied Learning

The following activity or experiment illustrates important concepts for this portion of the coursework. Please make note of the scientific aspects of the activity as well as the specific areas of focus. These should reinforce important concepts and definitions that you have learned as you apply them.

## Science

Strength of materials — stress

## Definition

Structural strength of loading members

## Parts List:

- Popsicle sticks (10)
- White glue

## Experiment(s):

You will be building two picture frame structures using popsicle sticks as the core material.

Begin building the first structure by laying four popsicle sticks flat. It should resemble a Tic-Tac-Toe shape but with enough room for an "X" in the middle. Build an identical structure; this time lay down another two popsicle sticks in an "X." See the picture below.

Take the frame you built by the corners and try to manipulate the shape of the frame. Repeat this with the second "X" frame.

## ☑ Take Away

The second frame with the "X" in the middle is structurally superior to the first frame. The "X" strengthened the frame by adding more supports that help absorb the load. The diagonals and the frame constitute a truss structure, which was a new feat in civil engineering (Pre-Industrial revolution). But God designed this long ago in human bones.

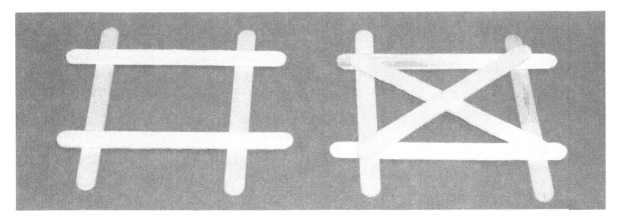

**Questions:**

1. If we change the "X" configuration to form a "plus" (+) sign instead of an "X," would this change the strength?

2. Observe/research man-made items with added structural support. List several shapes/configurations you observed that were used to increase strength beyond a simple frame.

## Ray Comfort's — Just for Fun!

Have someone hold one arm straight out to the side, palm down, and instruct him to maintain this position. Then place two fingers on his wrist and push down. He'll resist. Now have him put one foot on a surface that's a half-inch higher (a few magazines) and repeat. This time his arm will not be able to resist. By misaligning his hips, you've offset his spine.

Put someone with his or her back to a wall with their heels touching the wall. Then place a dollar bill at his (or her) feet and say, "You can have that dollar if you can pick it up without moving your feet."

## Concepts and Definitions

The following information will lay a critical foundation for related Applied Learning activities. It is important that you read and understand this information so the Applied Learning opportunities can demonstrate and clarify important scientific concepts in action.

Friction is created as two objects come in contact with each other and a frictional force is generated as the surface of one object is pushed along the other object's surface. In other words, one object is rubbing another object, otherwise known as friction.

There is more to friction than two objects that rub one another. The object's weight and the texture of the contact surface play a factor in determining the frictional force. This is defined in the equation below which looks interestingly like the word "FUN," but actually is defined as the following:

$$F_{friction} = \mu N$$

Where:

F > Frictional Force:

The resistive force of an object as it opposes the direction of movement of another object (see figure below).

μ > Coefficient of Friction:

The coefficient of friction is a number, which is derived through laboratory testing and is tabulated for different combinations of materials. Numbers change as combinations of materials are used.

Here are two examples:

| Material 1: | Wood | Teflon |
|---|---|---|
| Material 2: | Concrete | Steel |
| | $\mu = 0.62$ | $\mu = 0.04$ |

Notice the difference between the coefficients of frictions (μ). Wood against concrete creates a much higher μ than Teflon against steel. The "μ" reveals that the wood and concrete combination will have a greater force of friction than the Teflon and steel combination. The greater the number (or closer to 1), the higher the frictional forces generated.

A quick way to get a general indication of the frictional properties is to touch or feel the material. You can sense the surface for texture/roughness. The rougher the surface, the more friction we can expect it to have.

N > Normal Force:

This is the weight of the object that is perpendicular to the contact surface.

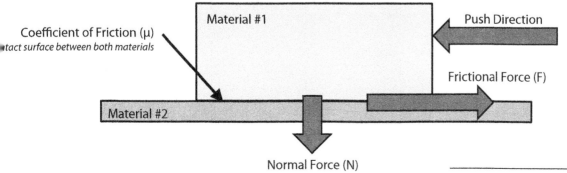

## Lubricant: The solution to alleviate friction:

A lubricant can be used to alleviate any frictional forces between any two surfaces. This is accomplished because a lubricant will act as an intermediary between both surfaces. It blocks by preventing direct contact between both surfaces, which reduces the frictional force (see figure below).

This is what our tear ducts do as we blink our eyes. Their function is to release fluid between the eyelid inner surface and eye surface to help prevent any friction buildup from occurring.

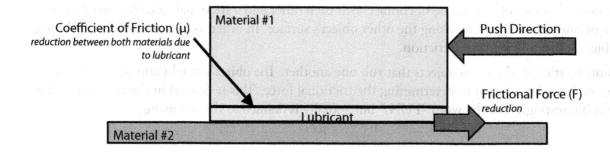

## Applied Learning

The following activity or experiment illustrates important concepts for this portion of the coursework. Please make note of the scientific aspects of the activity as well as the specific areas of focus. These should reinforce important concepts and definitions that you have learned as you apply them.

## Science

Friction

## Definition

Contact between any two surfaces will cause a force to be generated.

## Parts List:

- None

## Experiment:

Gently pinch the skin of your eyelid. Slightly pull it down so that your eyelid covers your eye, slightly resting on your bottom eyelashes. Hold it there for a few seconds. You will sense fluid over your eyelid. For the same effect, blink your eyes as fast as you can for five seconds.

## ☑ Take Away

Your tear ducts are located beneath your eyelid and excrete fluid on to your eyeball as you blink your eye or when your eyelid closes over your eye. This automatic function keeps them lubricated and reduces the frictional forces and also helps clear debris.

Blinking our eyes or having our eyes tear up automatically is something we take for granted because it just happens without any effort on our part. But a mechanical engineer by the name of Bob Kearns thought this would be a great idea for windshield wipers in the 1950s. He patented the electronic variable timer circuit so that vehicle wipers could be adjusted according to the rainfall.

**Questions:**

1.  What would happen if our eyes did not automatically generate fluid when we close our eyes?

2.  How many tear ducts are at the edge of each eyelid?

3.  Calculate the coefficient of friction for F = 100 lbs and N = 200 lbs.

4.  Calculate the frictional force of a 50-pound block of wood as it slides horizontally on concrete. (See previous section to obtain coefficient of friction.)

5.  List another example where a lubricant is used to reduce frictional forces.

## Applied Learning

The following activity or experiment illustrates important concepts for this portion of the coursework. Please make note of the scientific aspects of the activity as well as the specific areas of focus. These should reinforce important concepts and definitions that you have learned as you apply them.

Shock waves are caused when an object reaches the speed of sound (approx. 761 mph at sea level). The air in front of the object cannot get out of the way fast enough and begins to compress (get squeezed) together to form a shock wave.

### Science:

Fluid dynamics

Shock waves

### Definition:

Movement of air

### Parts List:

- Candle
- Candle lighter or match (adult supervision advised)
- Plastic water bottle (empty 500 mL)

### Experiment:

1. Place the candle on a table.
2. Remove the cap from the empty water bottle.
3. Carefully light the candle on the table (with adult supervision).
4. Stand about one foot away from the candle and hold the empty water bottle with the open end facing the candle (the closed bottom end of the water bottle facing you).
5. Stand behind the water bottle, holding firmly in one hand the upper portion of the bottle. Give a firm openhanded thump to the bottom of the bottle while looking at the candle's flame. (Make sure not to crush the water bottle; if you do, hit it more softly.)
6. The candle flame should extinguish. If it doesn't, move a little closer until the flame is extinguished.

☑ **Take Away**

The thumping action on the bottom of the empty water bottle generates a shock wave in the air. The shock wave travels in the direction of the candle and extinguishes the candle's flame.

## Question:

1. What was the farthest distance from the candle where the shock wave ceased to have an effect on the candle's flame?

## Applied Learning

The following activity or experiment illustrates important concepts for this portion of the coursework. Please make note of the scientific aspects of the activity as well as the specific areas of focus. These should reinforce important concepts and definitions that you have learned as you apply them.

## Science

Mechanics of materials

Structural integrity

## Definition

Everything we see, regardless of size, is designed to withstand a specific applied load (or force).

## Parts List:

*   Piece of cardboard
*   Sandbox (park) or sand (beach)
*   Water

## Experiment:

You will be going on a small trip for this one, either to a sandbox at your local park or a sandy beach.

Begin constructing a tunnel in the sand using water, making a mud-type paste. Now construct another tunnel the exact same size as the first, but this time put a piece of cardboard on the inside.

Take your cardboard and roll it to resemble the letter "U." Place the U-shaped cardboard upside down into the sand. Begin packing down the mud on top of the cardboard, creating the remainder of the tunnel.

## ☑ Take Away

The cardboard was used to create a hard lining to the tunnel, which supported all the sand on top and on the sides (just like the shipworm's secretion of a calcareous lining). Without it, the tunnel would collapse upon itself.

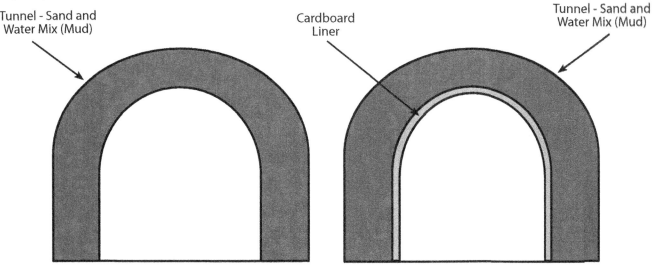

Tunnel - Sand and Water Mix (Mud)  •  Cardboard Liner  •  Tunnel - Sand and Water Mix (Mud)

## Questions:

1. Can you think of another type of material we could use instead of cardboard?

2. See how much weight you can place on top of both tunnels before they collapse.

## Applied Learning

The following activity or experiment illustrates important concepts for this portion of the coursework. Please make note of the scientific aspects of the activity as well as the specific areas of focus. These should reinforce important concepts and definitions that you have learned as you apply them.

## Science

Optics

## Definition

Reflection of light

## Parts List:

- Cylindrical can with lid (potato chip can is convenient)
- Clear plastic report cover
- Clear tape
- Scissors
- Plastic food wrap
- Small transparent beads
- Small pieces of shiny confetti or paper
- Drill or nail and hammer (adult supervision required)
- Sandpaper (optional)

## Experiment:

We will be building a kaleidoscope to demonstrate this fun optics experiment.

- If using a drill, please have an adult help you drill a small hole through the bottom of the can. If using a nail and hammer, proceed to the next step.
- With proper supervision or with the help of an adult, carefully use a nail and hammer to tap a small hole in the bottom of the can. Ensure there are no sharp edges. Sandpaper is optional.
- Fold a clear plastic report cover into an equilateral triangle (4.5" sides) lengthwise and tape. Be careful, as the plastic can be sharp.
- Remove the lid and insert clear triangle. Trim the length to match height of can.
- Lay the plastic food wrap on the open end and push down slightly into the can to create a pouch.
- Place transparent beads and shiny confetti into your new plastic pouch.
- Put the lid back on with the edge of the lid keeping the plastic wrap snug to the lid and can.
- Tilt the can upward toward a source of light and rotate the can while looking through the hole.
- Enjoy your newly created kaleidoscope.

☑  **Take Away**

The images of the beads and confetti reflect off the sides of the triangular plastic report cover. The result is a distorted vision of the reflections of the materials, coupled with the source of light coming through the lid of the can.

However, the opposite is true of the moth because their abundance of exterior tiny ridges and bumps change the direction of light. Our experiment with the interior triangle is just a few angles. But in the moth, every angle that light could hit seems to disappear as if absorbed. Capturing light distorts light as in our kaleidoscope. Capturing light for researchers could lead to better solar energy in the future.

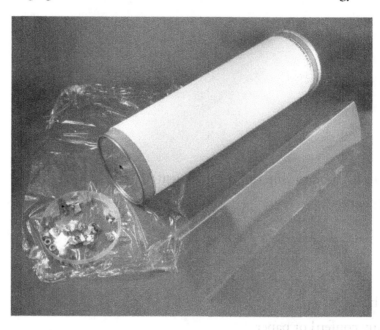

**Questions:**

1. What other items can you add which will give a different reflective image? Which ones work better than others and why?

2. Do you think you would have the same results if the can was a shorter length?

3. What other type of surfaces have a reflective property?

## Applied Learning

The following activity or experiment illustrates important concepts for this portion of the coursework. Please make note of the scientific aspects of the activity as well as the specific areas of focus. These should reinforce important concepts and definitions that you have learned as you apply them.

Photosynthesis is the conversion of energy. Energy can neither be created nor destroyed.

Energy is converted from one form to the other. This is the first law of thermodynamics.

This is observed in living plants and their relationship to the sun.

Sun > provides light (energy) to the green plants > green plants convert this light energy into a chemical energy (carbohydrates = sugar)

**Summary:** First law of thermodynamics as light energy is converted to chemical energy

Exactly how did that happen?

1. Leaf absorbs water from the plant's root system

2. Leaf absorbs gas from the air (carbon dioxide or $CO_2$)

3. Leaf receives light energy from the sun

4. Chloroplasts (which contain the chlorophyll) convert the sun's energy into a chemical energy

5. The chemical energy combined with $CO_2$ (carbon dioxide) and $H_2O$ (water) produces both oxygen and sugar

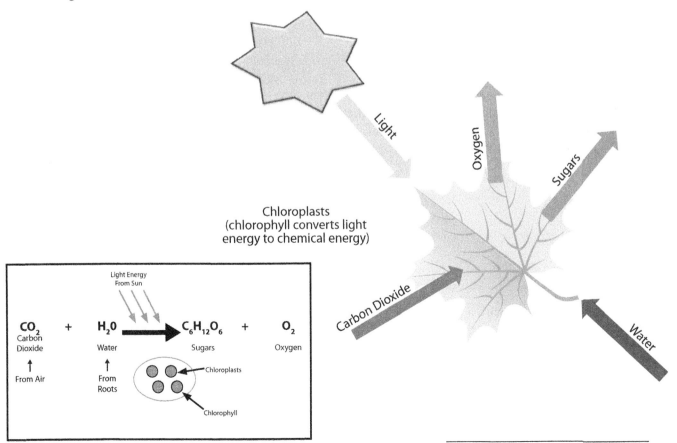

Chloroplasts
(chlorophyll converts light
energy to chemical energy)

## Science
Photosynthesis

### Definition
The process of a leaf as it generates sugars and oxygen

### Parts List:
- A fresh-cut leaf
- Bowl of water

### Experiment:
Drop the leaf gently into the bowl of water without creating any bubbles. Place the bowl on a windowsill or outside in direct sunlight and leave it there for an hour.

### ☑ Take Away
You will notice air bubbles being created in the water after a period of time. These bubbles are oxygen bubbles that are given off by the plant, which is a byproduct of the photosynthesis process.

Researchers are green with envy at the thought of the possibility of an artificial leaf that is capable of storing energy. This complex system starts with chloroplasts. Unfortunately, this is the start, and researchers have been unable to replicate chloroplasts to get off the starting blocks. Thinking outside the box, scientists looked to the leaf. Their experiment encompassed a more complicated version of our experiment with a container of water, sunlight, an artificial leaf, and oxygen and hydrogen bubbles being released.

### Questions:
1. How important is sunlight to the photosynthesis process? Repeat the same experiment, only this time try storing the leaf in a dark area away from any light. Were oxygen bubbles still produced when there was an absence of light?

2. Try this experiment with a different type of leaf. Were the results the same?

## Applied Learning

The following activity or experiment illustrates important concepts for this portion of the coursework. Please make note of the scientific aspects of the activity as well as the specific areas of focus. These should reinforce important concepts and definitions that you have learned as you apply them.

## Science

Mathematical sequences

Fibonacci sequence

## Definition

The Fibonacci sequence is observed in plant life.

## Parts List:

• Plants

## Experiment:

Take a stroll in a park or plant nursery. Observe the plants closely and list those you think have the Fibonacci sequence, which is the golden ratio angle of 137.5 degrees.

☑ **Take Away**

Think about how a plant grows, and take some time to marvel at the mathematical precision. Living plants follow set rules as to the location and height of the next leaf generated. These are not accidents and certainly not random but an ordered process that our God dictates.

**Questions:**

1. Have you ever seen a plant with all the leaves on one side only?

2. Do you see a general shape or pattern that plant leaves seem to follow? Take some time to explain your observation.

3. Do all leaves have a center spine?

**Ray Comfort's — Just for Fun!**

Get a pen and paper and say, "I bet I can say a number that you can't write down within five seconds. Here's the number: eleven thousand, eleven hundred and eleven."

Say, "Think of any number below 10. Double the number. Add 6 to it. Cut the number in half. Take away the number you first chose from the number you now have."

# Quizzes Section

| | *Discovery of Design* | Quiz 1 | Scope: | Total score: | Name |
|---|---|---|---|---|---|
| **Q** | Concepts & Comprehension | | Chapters 1–2 | ____of 100 | |

## Answer Questions: (5 Points Each Question)

1. What is the name of the science where designs are developed from designs in nature?

2. How do many microscopic life forms propel themselves through liquids?

3. What are bacterial batteries?

4. What is an example of biofilms helping to block invading foreign bacteria?

5. What does the author mean by "designer diatoms"?

6. What happens when light shines on the plant-based proteins on an electricity-conducting glass surface?

7. Which insect is named in the Bible verse Exodus 10:4?

8. When it comes to ants, what determines the overall group behavior?

9. Where are several species of brilliant white beetles found?

10. What chemical does the bombardier beetle's spray and rocket fuel have in common?

11. What is the process called that cosmetic companies are using to mimic the light wave properties of butterfly and to replace the use of pigments, dyes, waxes, and oils?

12. What physical feature makes dragonflies unusual among insects?

13. What does a firefly create by mixing chemicals in its abdomen?

14. What is an additional potential benefit for hearing aids created by studying the fly?

15. How does light travel through the eye of a bee?

16. What do insects like grasshoppers or moths hear with their ultra-sensitive listening systems?

17. What is the major advantage of small, multi-leg robots over actual insects?

18. How does the beetle "drink" the water collected?

19. Why is synthetic spider silk one of the most sought after technologies in biomimicry?

20. Why are the termite mounds built by *Macrotermes michaelseni* of interest to architects?

21. What is another name for the chipper chain?

22. Why was paper so expensive centuries ago?

## Bonus Questions: (10 Points Each Question)

1. How were big trees harvested before chainsaws were invented?

2. How do water striders move so rapidly on water?

## Answer Questions: (5 Points Each Question)

1. What is the name of the strategy bats use to catch insects?

2. What do engineers use the flight-swim formula for?

3. How does the design of *Sharovipteryx mirabilis* create a problem for evolutionists?

4. What problem did Japan's rail system have that scientists looked to the kingfisher to solve?

5. Owls have what kind of special feathers that allow flight at slow, quiet speeds?

6. What makes it possible for swifts to perform acrobatic moves while flying?

7. Describe the design of the toucan's beak.

8. Describe the skin of a boxfish.

9. What have the engineers at Bell Labs concluded about the design of the microlenses of the brittlestar?

10. What has the military prepared based on the color-changing design of the cuttlefish?

11. How can the elephant nose fish design be applied to airbag deployment safety?

12. What is an important goal for ships?

13. What has copied the lobster's eye design?

14. Why is the adhesive produced by mussels remarkable?

15. What do scientists recognize about the octopus arm?

16. What kind of medical applications do scientists hope to achieve by copying the design of the seashell?

17. What function do scientists believe the anti-microbial chemical protein detected in sea slugs have in addition to repelling certain predators?

18. What is a major problem with commercial optical fiber?

19. What challenges do designers of submarines face?

20. What does the blunt nose of both sperm whales and submarines result in?

## Bonus Questions: (10 Points Each Question)

1. Since swifts do not perch on tree branches, where do they build their nests?

2. How can the beak of a woodpecker survive hammering?

## Answer Questions: (5 Points Each Question)

1. Were animals living in the distant past primitive and simple?

2. What are scientists studying about antler regeneration?

3. What did Sperry manufacture?

4. What acrobatic abilities do geckos have?

5. How do giraffes keep from fainting when raising and lowering their heads several feet?

6. What have scientists found when they have modeled the horse bone and then applied pressure?

7. What do welders use that is based on the design of penguins?

8. What dual mechanisms allow tree frogs to hang upside down on leaves, regardless of whether the surface is dry, wet, smooth, or rough?

9. What do mosquitoes zero in on?

10. What do scientists hope DNA can help with in the future?

11. Describe how the ear processes sound as noted by Bell.

12. What may someday be commonplace for secure identification purposes?

13. How are vessels near a wound sealed off?

14. What is the purpose of the elliptical swirls of a fingerprint?

15. What is unusual about how the ball joint fits into the hip socket in humans?

16. What permits controlled rotation and flexing for our arms?

17. Do small cuts inside the mouth tend to heal more or less quickly than external injuries?

18. How can aircraft components and medical implants heal themselves?

19. Name the strongest material in our bodies.

20. What is the skin of an infant covered with before birth?

## Bonus Questions: (10 Points Each Question)

1. What is it about the color orange that makes a useful light filter?

2. How do tree frogs act as barometers?

## Answer Questions: (5 Points Each Question)

1. What art form resembles the folding of a beech leaf?

2. What percentage of modern drugs originally come from plants or plant derivatives?

3. What did Swiss engineer Georges de Mestral invent based on the close inspection of cockleburs?

4. What do forisomes do within the capillary tubes of the bean plant?

5. What is the behavior called where plants generate chemical defenses against competing plants?

6. What did the German chemical company BASF create by duplicating the lotus leaf surface?



7. What was the first barbed wire business called?



8. What inspired the creation of smart clothing?



9. What did Christopher Columbus notice on one of his several sailing voyages to North America?



10. What is a potential application of the skunk cabbage?



11. How have scientists tapped into the ability of plants in the manufacture of solar cells?

12. What food packaging application could be created by polymers mimicking the Venus flytrap?

13. On what pattern of support did Paxton base the Crystal Palace?

14. Why do scientists suggest the wheat fiber mechanism be copied?

15. What are buckyballs currently used as?

16. How does nano-scale technology offer promising solutions to the water-borne pathogen problem?

17. How are laboratory created synthetic opals being used?

18. How are pulsars useful?




19. Give an example of a spiral shape found in nature.




20. What are some of the practical uses for the PAX impeller blades?




## Bonus Questions: (10 Points Each Question)

1. What other plants are carnivorous, or insectivorous, besides the Venus flytrap?




2. What was inside the Crystal Palace?

| T | *Discovery of Design*<br>Concepts & Comprehension | Test | Scope:<br>Chapters 1–8 | Total score:<br>____of 100 | Name |

## Answer Questions: (4 Points Each Question)

1. What are bacterial batteries?

2. What is an example of biofilms helping to block invading foreign bacteria?

3. What chemical does the bombardier beetle's spray and rocket fuel have in common?

4. What is the major advantage of small, multi-leg robots over actual insects?

5. Why are the termite mounds built by *Macrotermes michaelseni* of interest to architects?

6. How does the design of *Sharovipteryx mirabilis* create a problem for evolutionists?

7. What problem did Japan's rail system have that scientists looked to the kingfisher to solve?

8. What have the engineers at Bell Labs concluded about the design of the microlenses of the brittlestar?

9. What has the military prepared based on the color changing design of the cuttlefish?

10. What kind of medical applications do scientists hope to achieve by copying the design of the seashell?

11. Were animals living in the distant past primitive and simple?

12. How do giraffes keep from fainting when raising and lowering their heads several feet?

13. What do welders use that is based on the design of penguins?

14. What dual mechanisms allow tree frogs to hang upside down on leaves, regardless of whether the surface is dry, wet, smooth, or rough?

15. What is unusual about how the ball joint fits into the hip socket in humans?

16. What percentage of modern drugs originally come from plants or plant derivatives?

17. What did Swiss engineer Georges de Mestral invent based on the close inspection of cockleburs?

18. What did the German chemical company BASF create by duplicating the lotus leaf surface?

19. What is a potential application of the skunk cabbage?

20. On what pattern of support did Paxton base the Crystal Palace?

**Bonus Questions:** (10 Points Each Question)

1.  How is the blood-clotting mechanism related to intelligent design?

2.  What causes the different colors of light?

## Short Answer Questions: (4 Points Each Answer)

1.  Different shapes exhibit different _____.

2.  Fish are created with a shape that minimizes _____.

3.  The arapaima fish has different _____of layers that account for its incredible armor-like _____.

4.  Not all materials break at the same _____ load.

5.  The seemingly fragile spider silk has a great tensile strength relative to its _____.

6.  _____ is the ability of a material to resist breaking when a force is applied.

7. _____ is the ability of a material to deflect and return back to its original shape.

8. _____ is the ability of a material to stretch without breaking.

9. _____ is the melting point of a material.

10. Steel, copper, silver, and gold are examples of _____.

11. Plastics, rubber, hair, nails, Silly Putty™, styrofoam, and plastic are examples of _____.

12. Bowls, plates, bricks, pipes, floor, and tiles are examples of _____.

13. Silicon, gallium, and arsenide are examples of _____.

14. Understanding the properties of a _____ will enable you to choose the best one for the task at hand.

15. _____ science is complex and far-reaching to a broad science base. It provides us with clever solutions to address new design requirements and create something new.

16. When water is removed from a material, the material will contract and change its shape and the result is a stiffer item. When water is added, the material stretches and becomes softer. _____ use this same principle in order to spread their seed as humidity decreases in the air.

17. With the ping-pong ball sitting on top of the paper, what we perceive as being a smooth piece of paper is, in fact, a _____ microscopic surface.

18. Understanding and harnessing what we can glean from the squid will contribute to _____ with the ability to maneuver in difficult mediums such as the viscous fluids in the human body.

19. Light consists of both an electric field and a _____ field traveling at right angles (90 degrees) to each other.

20. The unit of measurement for _____ is called Hertz or abbreviated as Hz.

21. No one can actually see the _____ moving across the room until it fills the room completely.

22. Speed of light = wavelength x _____

23. White light is made up of _____ different color components.

24. A sine wave is described as having both a _____ and trough.

25. How many degrees are in a sine wave?

## Short Answer Questions: (4 Points Each Answer)

1. _____ is the branch of physics that deals with the behavior of light.

When the incident ray hits the surface it will do one of following: (Draw a line to the correct answer.)

2. It will be reflected            > Reflected ray and refracted

3. It will be absorbed            > Refracted ray

4. It will be both            > Reflected

5. There is a relationship that is used to predict the outcome of an incident ray as it comes in contact with a surface. This relationship is called _____ law.

6. The _____ of refraction is a ratio of the speed of light in a vacuum to the speed of light in the substance.

7. The field of view in a _____ is much smaller than the field of view of the human eye.

8. _____ is the science that assigns a numerical value to different variables to make sense of a problem.

9. God has created humans with _____ skills.

10. How many computer viruses are found every day?

11. Our _____ is the most complex organ in our body.

12. Interestingly, the brain occupies a _____ volume in proportion to its role and significance.

13. Scientists are trying to understand and copy the human brain's ability to communicate through _____.

14. If 42 semi-trailers represent the visual processing system (1/10th) of the brain, how many semi-trailers would you need to represent the whole brain?

15. All light travels in what is called a _____ wave shape.

16. Every _____ in the visible spectrum has its own wavelength associated with it.

17. The light that we can see with our eyes is called the _____ light spectrum and it ranges from 400 nm to 700 nm.

18. Any wavelengths that are below 400 nm are classified as _____ (or UV) and any wavelengths above 700 nm are classified as infrared (or IR).

19. Approximately what wavelength would a blue jay bird have?

20. The core of _____ deals with the science behind the mixing of two or more substances together and observing the newly formed compound.

21. A _____ is what is formed after a chemical reaction has occurred. These are the chemicals present at the end of the reaction.

22. How far can the bombardier beetle spray?

23. What is a hertz?

24. _____ of sound is measured based on a ratio between a measured and referenced power level.

25. _____ are lightest and therefore they get there first. This allows them to clump not only to each other but also to the break in the blood vessel, which speeds up healing.

## Short Answer Questions: (4 Points Each Answer)

1. The sensitivity of our _____ is incredible.

2. There isn't anything to date that rivals the adhesive properties of the _____.

3. Velcro uses a nylon hook-and-loop combination to _____ the load. The result has been so successful that NASA has utilized Velcro on space shuttle missions.

4. _____ come in many forms and can be used to bond various materials together.

5. The wasp's saliva contains _____, which help bond the wood fibers together to make their nest.

6. The _____ pigment layer of a cat's eyes lend to their shining appearance when they are illuminated in the dark as is their namesake, the Catseye road reflector.

7. _____ is the unified relationship between electricity and magnetism.

8. Since electromagnetism is the creation of a magnetic field when there is an electric current, we can create magnets by running electricity through wires wrapped around _____.

9. Electrostatic forces are identified as either a _____ or an electron, depending on their polarity.

10. Opposite polarities _____.

11. _____ is defined as the mass (weight) per unit volume.

12. _____ slows down and is a hindrance in the flow of fluid.

## Short Answer Questions: (7 Points Each Answer)

13. What types of industry would be revolutionized if scientists could replicate the mussel's sticking power?

14. Name other materials besides nylon which are being used to fabricate Velcro.

15. Compare modern papermaking to wasp papermaking. Which is superior and why?

16. What is the scientific term for the small forces that the gecko's spatula generates?

## Short Answer Questions: (4 Points Each Answer)

1. The mass flow of the fluid will be _____ at the inlet (front), throat (middle), and outlet (back).

2. The fluid density of any fluid is the measure of _____ per cubic volume.

3. The termite mounds do not need any help to achieve conservation of mass flow. However, the Eastgate Mall needs a little help in this area. What does the mall require to keep the air flowing so that the air does not become stagnant and warm?

4. A _____ structure was a new feat in civil engineering (Pre-Industrial Revolution), but God designed this long ago in human bones.

5. _____ is created as two objects come into contact with each other and a frictional force is generated as the surface of one object is pushed along the other object's surface.

6. There is more to friction than two objects that rub one another. The objects _____ and the texture of the contact surface play a factor in determining the frictional force.

7. The coefficient of friction is a _____, which is derived through laboratory testing and is tabulated for different combinations of materials. Numbers change as combinations of materials are used.

8. The _____ the surface, the more friction we can expect it to have.

9. A _____ can be used to alleviate any frictional forces between any two surfaces.

10. Blinking our eyes or having our eyes tear up automatically is something we take for granted because it just happens without any effort on our part. What did a mechanical engineer by the name of Bob Kearns invent in the 1950s based on this design?

11. What would happen if our eyes did not automatically generate fluid when we close our eyes?

12. How many tear ducts are at the edge of each eyelid?

13. List another example where a lubricant is used to reduce frictional forces.

14. Shock waves are caused when an object reaches the speed of _____ (approximately 761 mph at sea level).

15. The air in front of the object cannot get out of the way fast enough and begins to _____ (get squeezed) together to form a shock wave.

16. Everything we see, regardless of size, is designed to withstand a specific applied _____ (or force).

17. Capturing _____ for researchers could lead to better solar energy in the future.

18. Photosynthesis is the conversion of energy. Energy can neither be created nor destroyed. Energy is converted form one form to the other. This is the first law of _____.

19. Researchers are green with envy at the thought of an artificial leaf that is capable of storing _____.

20. Unfortunately, researchers have been unable to replicate _____.

21. How important is sunlight to the photosynthesis process?

22. The Fibonacci sequence is observed in _____ life.

23. Living plants follow set _____ as to the location and height of the next leaf generated. These are not accidents and certainly not random, but an ordered process that our God dictates.

24. Do you see a general shape or pattern that plant leaves seem to follow? Explain your observation.

25. Do all leaves have a center spine?

# Short Answer Questions: (5 Points Each Blank)

1. Fish are created with a shape that minimizes _____.

2. _____ is the ability of a material to deflect and return back to its original shape.

3. When water is removed from a material, the material will contract and change its shape and the result is a stiffer item. When water is added, the material stretches and becomes softer. _____ use this same principle in order to spread their seed as humidity decreases in the air.

4. Understanding and harnessing what we can glean from the squid will contribute to _____ with the ability to maneuver in difficult mediums such as the viscous fluids in the human body.

5. White light is made up of _____ different color components.

6. _____ is the branch of physics that deals with the behavior of light.

7. The field of view in a _____ is much smaller than the field of view of the human eye.

8. Our _____ is the most complex organ in our body.

9. The core of _____ deals with the science behind the mixing of two or more substances together and observing the newly formed compound.

10. How far can the bombardier beetle spray?

11. The sensitivity of our _____ is incredible.

12. The wasp's saliva contains _____, which help bond the wood fibers together to make their nest.

13. The _____ pigment layer of a cat's eyes lend to their shining appearance when they are illuminated in the dark as is their namesake, Cat's eye road reflector.

14. _____ is the unified relationship between electricity and magnetism.

15. _____ slows down and is a hindrance in the flow of fluid.

16. The termite mounds do not need any help to achieve conservation of mass flow. However, the Eastgate Mall needs a little help in this area. What does the mall require to keep the air flowing so that the air does not stay stagnant and warm?

17. Blinking our eyes or having our eyes tear up automatically is something we take for granted because it just happens without any effort on our part. What did a mechanical engineer by the name of Bob Kearns invent in the 1950s based on this design?

18. Shock waves are caused when an object reaches the speed of _____ (approximately 761 mph at sea level).

19. Photosynthesis is the conversion of energy. Energy can neither be created nor destroyed. Energy is converted form one form to the other. This is the first law of _____.

20. Do you see a general shape or pattern that plant leaves seem to follow? Explain your observation.

# Answer Keys

# *Discovery of Design* — Worksheet Answer Keys

## Introduction

1. Biomimicry

2. Millions of years of supposed evolutionary change developed these innovations; valuable, practical designs have been with us since the beginning of time

3. Patterns and information are conserved with the passing of generations, but the DNA blueprint does not increase in complexity or gain new information.

4. The historic definition of science is the search for knowledge and truth about the physical world, wherever this may lead.

5. Design examples show us how to properly care for nature and maintain its health; the other purpose was for the benefit of living things, and also that ideas could be discovered and utilized for the welfare of mankind.

## Chapter 1 – Worksheet 1

1. 1657

2. Using molecular motors

3. 10 million

4. flagellus, central shaft of protein, electrochemical reactions

5. This organism has hundreds of tiny nozzles covering its outer surface. It manufactures a slime that shoots from these nozzles, much like silly string. As a result, the bacterium recoils in the opposite direction using the principle of jet propulsion.

6. The prefixes *micro* and *nano* come from Greek roots meaning, respectively, "small" and "dwarf." Technically, micro stands for one millionth, or $10^{-6}$. The, thickness of a sheet of paper is about 4000 micro-inches. A nano is defined as one billionth, or $10^{-9}$. In one inch there are one million micro-inches, and one billion nano-inches.

7. Typical speed for a household electric fan is 1500 rpm. This is 60 times slower than the speed of the bacteria flagellum.

8. Silly string was first introduced as a child's toy in 1972. A liquid polymer in a pressurized aerosol container quickly turns solid when exposed to air. Polymers are compounds with long chains of chemically bonded molecules. One container can produce silly string hundreds of feet long.

## Chapter 1 – Worksheet 2

1. This tiny microbe produces electrical current using simple sugars as its fuel source.

2. 80%

3. Energy-producing microorganisms

4. To combine the electric output from a large number of these bacteria to produce a practical level of current.

5. One cup

6. A battery is a chemical cell useful for storing electrical energy. Energy storage is a challenge for technology, and research continues on batteries with high efficiency and capacity.

7. When fuel is burned in a car to produce motion, much of the resulting heat energy is unused. This heat radiates outward from the engine and water coolant, and also leaves with the hot exhaust gases. The second law of thermodynamics describes such inevitable losses in every energy transfer process.

8. A light bulb, whether in a flashlight or reading lamp, has an electric current of about one ampere. This amounts to over six million-trillion electrons (actually $6.25 \times 10^{18}$) passing through the bulb filament each second. These electrons move through the filament at a snail's pace, somewhat similar to a large crowd passing through a narrow gate.

## Chapter 1 – Worksheet 3

1. Large organized communities of bacteria

2. By releasing chemicals

3. Signal blocking

4. Protecting animals like dogs and cattle from cholera infection, or biofilms added to paint to prevent barnacles from attaching to the surface of boats

5. to use biofilms to control corrosion in oil and gas pipelines

6. Living bacteria are everywhere in large numbers, and there may well be millions on each of our hands. Most are harmless "resident bacteria," but hand washing is a good practice to prevent the spread of less friendly bacteria. Many bacteria reproduce and multiply in less than a single hour.

7. A layer of biofilm often coats rocks in streams, making their surfaces slippery. Also, biofilms sometimes cover the surface of stagnant ponds.

8. Colorful biofilms are found on the surface of hot, acidic pools in Yellowstone National Park, as well as on glaciers. In homes, biofilm colonies may grow in the corners of shower stalls.

## Chapter 1 – Worksheet 4

1. Diatoms are microscopic, single-celled algae.

2. They are found in the sea, freshwater lakes, and soil.

3. They are looking for ready-made components.

4. Magnesium oxide MgO; and titanium oxide TiO.

5. These are diatoms that researchers hope to encourage growth into new and useful shapes.

6. Diatoms have been variously classified as plants, animals, or something in between. They share biochemical features of both plants and animals, including photosynthesis and mobility.

7. Glass consists of the chemical compound silicon dioxide, $SiO_2$. The mineral name is quartz or silica.

8. This common chalk-like material serves as a filter for liquids and an abrasive. Its absorbent property is also useful as a component in kitty litter. In addition, diatomaceous earth serves as a stabilizer in explosives, as a mechanical insecticide, and as a medium for potted plants.

## Chapter 1 – Worksheet 5

1. Photosynthesis

2. Plants

3. Photosynthetic proteins

4. The lights causes a faint current of electricity to pass thru adjacent layers and by putting multiple layers in series, the plant-based protein generates a useful electrical current.

5. One advantage is the ability to repair itself when damage occurs because plants are self-healing.

6. Current is the flow of electrons through a conductor, measured in amperes. A typical light bulb may use one amp of current. The current produced by a single spinach protein is on the order of a billionth of an ampere, or one nanoamp ($10^{-9}$ amp).

7. Solar heating of portions of the earth causes breezes to blow. Wind then results as air moves to even out temperature and pressure differences. The sun also causes water to evaporate from lakes. This water later condenses and flows back downhill, where it may be harnessed by generators for hydroelectricity. Fossil fuels include coal, oil, and natural gas. It is thought that these fuels largely formed from earlier plants that captured sunlight by photosynthesis. The vegetation later was buried and compressed by pressure and heat. Fossil fuels are thus solar energy stored up from the past.

8. Nuclear energy is available from elements inside the earth, and geothermal energy comes from underground magma. Tidal movement, caused by the moon's gravity, is also tapped as an energy source.

## Chapter 2 Introduction– Worksheet 1

1. Undiscovered creatures or insects in tropical rain forest regions.

2. Insect

3. Invertebrates

4. Locusts

5. Any of the following: ants, beetles, flies, spiders, centipedes

## Chapter 2 – Worksheet 1

1. Swarming

2. Countless interactions between nearby ants

3. Contact with antenna and shared smells; information on home base of ants, nest repair needs, food sources, predators, and more

4. Problem solving

5. Can include management of major airports or telephone networks, mail distribution, computer search engines, managing truck fleets, or even boardroom decisions.

6. Like all insects, ants have three pairs of legs, totaling six. Myrmecology is the scientific study of ants, a branch of entomology, or insect science. The Greek word for ant is *myrmex*.

7. Ants are the most numerous animal worldwide. They comprise 15–25 percent of the total animal biomass or weight. The combined weight of all living ants far outweighs the earth's total human population.

8. Proverbs 6:6–8 describes the diligent work of the ant. This insect provides us with an example of ambition and planning for the future.

## Chapter 2 – Worksheet 2

1. Southeast Asia

2. *Cyphochilus*

3. Chitin

4. Their random orientation reflects light waves to all directions and all visible wavelengths to create the white color.

5. Can include artificial light-scattering filaments replace minerals used to brighten paper, or coating for the inside of a light bulb to be more efficient

6. Bleach is added in an early stage of the paper-making process. Later, various white pigments may also be added, including the chemical titanium oxide, $TiO^2$.

7. Chitin (KI-tin) is the common shell-like covering of many insects, and is also found on crustaceans such as lobsters. Chitin is a long-chain polymer with the chemical formula $(C_8H_{13}O_5N)_n$.

8. To avoid predators, the color of this beetle matches its frequent habitat, bright white fungi. How the fungi itself produces this color is yet

another marvel that is not well understood. The beetle's reflective surface also provides cooling for its body.

## Chapter 2 – Worksheet 3

1. Its defense mechanism of being able to produce repeated chemical explosions in its abdomen and then spray hot vaporized fluid out and aimed in almost any direction.

2. 65 feet (20 m) per second

3. Hydrogen peroxide ($H_2O_2$)

4. Gas turbine engines sometimes quit during flight and have to be reignited quickly

5. Rocket technology, and automobile air bag systems

6. Hydrogen peroxide, $H_2O_2$, is useful for cleaning and sterilizing wounds. This chemical is also a disinfectant and bleaching agent.

7. Bombardiers and similar beetles are found on every continent except Antarctica. The beetles inhabit woodlands and often live beneath leaves or stones.

8. "Just so" stories are suggested whereby the beetle's defense mechanism developed slowly over many generations. In truth, the beetle is an example of irreducible complexity in nature.

## Chapter 2 – Worksheet 4

1. Morpho rheterno

2. Scales make up the wings, and when light penetrates the layers, only the blue color is reflected back. The blues blend and other color wavelengths cancel each other out.

3. The constructive and destructive interference of light waves

4. The butterfly effect

5. Car paint, credit card security, optical computing

6. Estimates total about 20,000 known species of butterfly. In many places, one hundred or more butterfly species are common, a highly unusual variety to coexist in one location.

7. Adult butterflies typically live for about one month.

8. The colors of light result from their different wavelengths. Wavelengths for visible light are very small, ranging between 0.7 and 0.4 microns for the colors red and blue. These wavelengths are about 0.0001 of an inch long, 100 times less than the thickness of a sheet of paper.

## Chapter 2 – Worksheet 5

1. Four distinct wings

2. Nearly 40 mph (64 km/hr)

3. Creates a whirl of air above the wing, reduces the air pressure slightly, creating needed lift for flight.

4. They appear not be moving at all.

5. Unmanned drones or surveillance aircraft to hover motionless, increased maneuverability, or aircraft being designed to carry more load than their own weight.

6. Dragonflies may live one to five years, most of it in the larvae stage. The larvae spend winters hibernating beneath the surface of lakes and ponds. The adult dragonfly lifetime is just a few months long and does not carry over a cold winter.

7. Dragonfly fossils are indeed found in many locations. The impressions in rock are close copies of living dragonflies, except that some fossils are ten times larger. The impressive fossil wingspans reach 30 inches (76 cm). Other than a reduction in size, dragonflies have not changed noticeably over time.

8. Dragonflies eat other insects, including flies, bees, and midges. They are sometimes called beneficial "mosquito hawks" because they help keep these pests in check.

## Chapter 2 – Worksheet 6

1. cold light

2. Luciferin or the enzme luciferase

3. Bioluminescence; chemiluminescence

4. More than 2000

5. glowworms

6. An adult firefly lives only about one week.

7. Both words come from Latin, "to bear light." The name Lucifer appears in Isaiah 14:12 as an indirect reference to Satan, who misrepresents himself as an angel of light according to 2 Corinthians 11:14.

8. Food and social interaction

## Chapter 2 – Worksheet 7

1. Their incredible ability to detect and track individual sounds

2. It finds one species of cricket to lay the eggs on.

3. We are able to tell direction of a sound because it arrives at the eardrums for each ear at slightly different times.

4. No

5. A smaller "fly-sized" hearing aid

6. The chirping rate of a cricket increases with temperature. Count the number of chirps in 15 seconds, then add the number 39 to find the Fahrenheit temperature. If 30 chirps are heard in 15 seconds (two per second), then the temperature is about 69°F (20.5°C).

7. Of our five senses — hearing, sight, smell, taste, and touch — hearing may be the most sensitive. A loudness level very close to zero decibels is noticeable. At this threshold of hearing, our eardrum moves only about the distance of a single atom. In addition, our sense of hearing is very rapid in its response. One can determine the direction of sound by which ear hears it first, a time difference of about 0.0004 seconds.

8. Yes, and unlike people, the eardrums of a fly are connected. A sound disturbance that impacts one eardrum quickly moves to the other, and from this the fly's brain is able to determine direction to the sound.

## Chapter 2 – Worksheet 8

1. Compound

2. *Ommatidia*

3. Light first enters through a micro lens, which caps the outer end of the column. The light then moves through the hollow column until it meets photoreceptors at the internal end.

4. They begin with a tiny lump of clear resin. Thousands of tiny bumps are formed on the

surface to function as lenses. Next, the resin is exposed to ultraviolet light. The surface lenses divide this light into many separate beams that move through the resin. Along the way the light polymerizes or chemically alters the resin. The result is permanent, side-by-side columns of light-guides within the resin, similar to the *ommatidia* of insects.

5. Miniature surveillance cameras and medical endoscopes

6. Each micro lens in a bee's eye has a narrow field of vision, somewhat like a flashlight beam. The partial images from the thousands of lenses blend together in an overlapping picture mosaic. Detail may be lacking, but any slight movement is readily detected. The color vision of bees lacks sensitivity to the color red, but they see more violet and ultraviolet light than the human eye.

7. A honeybee has about 7,000 separate lenses in an eye less than one millimeter across. This means that a single lens is about a micron in size, less than the thickness of a sheet of paper.

8. Ultraviolet light, or UV, has a wavelength less than that of visible light. It is also called black light and is more energetic than the familiar visible colors. Ultraviolet light can be used to sterilize medical instruments.

## Chapter 2 – Worksheet 9

1. Atomic Force Microscope; obtains images of samples on the smallest scale of present technology

2. It sometimes alters the delicate surface being explored.

3. Faint vibrations

4. Scientists are using the Atomic Force Microscope to find out how insects are able to "see" and "hear" vibrations.

5. The goal is the study of delicate biological materials without altering them in the process to lead to the improvement of the AFM.

6. The AFM was developed in 1986 by scientists Calvin Quate and Christoph Gerber. Both men have won many awards for microscope advancements.

7. The AFM "feels" surfaces rather than sees them. It resolves objects down to one angstrom in size, or $10^{-10}$ meter. This is the size of an individual atom, and the AMF shows the arrangement of individual atoms in crystal structures such as salt, sodium chloride.

8. There are several varieties of microscopes designed for various purposes. The earliest is the optical microscope. It uses visible light and resolves objects as small as 0.00001 inch, or 0.4 microns. Electron microscopes use a beam of electrons to produce three-dimensional images of objects as small as a few angstroms, slightly larger than an atom. Other instruments include the stereo microscope, atomic mass microscope, and the scanning tunneling microscope.

## Chapter 2 – Worksheet 10

1. Wheels and mechanical legs

2. These remotely operated vehicles can get stuck in sand like *Opportunity* did for five weeks in 2005.

3. At the Berkeley PEDAL lab, cockroaches and centipedes are filmed as they run on miniature treadmills. Tiny "jet packs" are attached to the insects to record their reaction when they are thrown off balance by sideways spurts of air. The insects are very talented at maintaining their balance, even while running on a rough surface. The insect legs typically function like tiny pogo sticks with a bouncing stride.

4. If the robot is overturned, the mechanical legs can be pivoted 180 degrees downward and the upside down machine can continue walking forward.

5. May include: exploration of other planet surfaces, explosive detection, cleanup of toxic spills, and other hazardous tasks

6. This word was coined by the Czech writer Karel Čapek in his play Rossum's *Universal Robots* (1923). The root refers to servitude or forced labor.

7. Many schools offer robotics training, ranging from a two-year technical degree, on through the doctoral level. Specialties include robotic design, assembly, programming, and management. There are opportunities in robotic manufacturing, education, and product development.

8. The name is French for "one hundred feet"; however, centipedes are not limited to this number. Instead, two legs appear on each body segment behind the head. The number of segments varies between 15 and 177, and is always an odd number. These numbers result in total leg numbers ranging from 28 to 352.

## Chapter 2 – Worksheet 11

1. African Stenocara beetle

2. An area that is desolate

3. Its bumpy outer wings collect and combine the tiny fog droplets from the frequent morning fog.

4. Upon reaching a certain size, the water droplets overcome electrostatic attraction forces and roll down the beetle's tilted back to its mouth.

5. a. water-attracting  b. water-repelling

6. All air holds moisture, even in a desert climate. When the temperature drops below the dew point, often in early morning, the air can no longer hold the moisture in suspension. Dew then precipitates from the air, forming droplets on cool surfaces.

7. The standard definition is a region with less than ten inches (25.4 cm) of precipitation annually. Harsh desert regions in the country of Namibia receive ten times less than this, just one inch of rain per year on average. Deserts are not always warm; frigid Antarctica is the world's largest desert because of its sparse snowfall.

8. They tap the sand with their tail ends to attract mates. This drumming can be heard by a nearby person, and human tapping can also attract beetles.

## Chapter 2 – Worksheet 12

1. As thin as 10 nanometers, or 10,000 times thinner than a human hair

2. To build webs, wrap prey, and to ride the wind to a new location

3. Can include: conduct light as a tiny version of fiber optics, ultrafast nanoscale optical circuits, microscopic test tubes, sensitive chemical detectors, and use in specialized microscopes with extreme magnification

4. How they make them essentially out of water and air, and how they keep their spinnerets from clogging

5. Because of possible improvements to everything from bulletproof vests to suspension cables for bridges

6. Many telescopes use a small, low-magnification finder scope to locate distant objects. Typically, there are crosshairs in the view of the finder that center on the desired object. In earlier years, these crosshairs were made from spider silk that was attached to a glass lens surface. Spider silk was the thinnest permanent material readily available for this purpose. Telescopes today often use laser light or computer tracking for sighting objects.

7. A nanotube is a wire-like structure that is usually made of a single layer of carbon atoms. The strands are 50,000 times thinner than the width of a human hair. They can extend several millimeters in length and have many uses in technology.

8. Suppose a steel wire is stretched to the same diameter as spider silk. The steel strand then is several times thinner than steel wool fiber. In this extreme limit of thinness, spider silk will support five times the weight of the equivalent steel fiber.

## Chapter 2 – Worksheet 13

1. The self-cooling systems these termites build into their termite mounds

2. Their food supply is a "farmed" fungus that must be kept at exactly 87°F (30°C). However, the outside temperature varies widely between 35 and 104°F (2–40°C).

3. To compensate, the termites open or close a series of internal heating and cooling vents. These vents connect numerous tunnels that maintain temperature along with ideal moisture and oxygen levels.

4. Zimbabwe

5. This 18-story shopping complex has no mechanical air conditioning or heating, yet remains comfortable. The interior ventilation system of ductwork is based on the structure of termite mounds. Outside breezes pull fresh air throughout the building.

6. Population studies of the termite mounds show as many as 15,000 adult occupants.

7. The termites constantly dig new tunnels and vents while plugging others with soil. In outlying areas of Africa, this grainy, reworked mound material is sometimes used for hard-packed floors.

8. Average annual temperature varies between 70°F (21°C) in summer and 57°F (14°C) in winter. The city of Harare is located 9° north of the equator.

## Chapter 2 – Worksheet 14

1. Wood sawyer

2. Small C-shaped jaws or mandibles on the beetles sliced cleanly through the wood fiber. The pair of sharp mandibles moved sideways in a pinching, scissors fashion.

3. Joseph Buford Cox

4. Oregon chain

5. The teeth cut much more efficiently than earlier saw designs.

6. Along with the axe, crosscut saws date back to Roman times. These saws cut horizontally through the tree trunk, across the grain. Such saws improved over time with new metal alloys and tooth design. They are still much used around the world, often with a woodsman on each end of the saw.

7. There are a large number of beetles, borers, and worms that damage wood. The timber beetle tends to prefer diseased trees, and is also attracted to cut logs. The best defense is healthy trees that repel and withstand invasive beetles.

8. Typical chainsaws for home use have a bar 14–20 inches long. Commercial forestry saws have bars 36 inches or longer. All chainsaws are dangerous to operate; the larger saws are powerful and heavy.

## Chapter 2 – Worksheet 15

1. It was made from cotton and linen rags and of limited quantity

2. René-Antoine Réaumur

3. Can include: plant fibers, wood fibers, or vegetation

4. Cellulose

5. Water, filler, and various new binder

6. The water-resistant nest consists of a gray or brown papery material. There are open hexagonal tubes for rearing the young, usually pointing downward. Small nests may be constructed in the eaves or corners of houses.

7. This complex chemical compound comprises about one-third of dry wood. Lignin is a major part of the cell walls of plants. The word comes from the Latin for wood.

8. Fine linen paper is made of cotton or linen fabric, beaten into fibers. Certain paper currency is also cloth-based.

## Chapter 2 – Worksheet 16

1. Gecko lizard

2. A waxy coating was once thought to be on their feet

3. *Micro setae*

4. 15 times

5. Miniature aquatic robots and non-wetting materials

6. Adult striders have wings that permit flight to nearby ponds.

7. Surface tension describes the "stickiness" of liquids. This is the tendency of molecules to adhere together and resist penetration. Water has a very high surface tension, allowing light objects to float. Liquid mercury also has a high surface tension.

8. The striders move by "digging" their feet into the water surface and generating vortices or tiny swirls. Pushing against the resulting "mini wall" of water, they recoil forward rapidly with speeds measured at five feet per second (1.5 meter/sec).

## Chapter 3 – Worksheet 1

1. Turtledove

2. Echolocation

3. Between 20 and 20,000 cycles per second or *hertz*

4. Parallel navigation

5. Sound Navigation and Ranging

6. Sound is defined as a vibration, whether produced by our vocal cords, violin strings, or thunder. In air, sound is a slight, rapidly changing pressure that is transmitted between the closely packed air molecules. The speed of sound in air depends on temperature, and averages about 1,100 feet per second, or 750 miles per hour (335 m/sec).

7. Also called a silent whistle, this device produces a sound frequency between 16,000 and 22,000 hertz. This frequency is at the top or somewhat beyond our human hearing range. Dogs and cats have small eardrums that can vibrate very rapidly and detect such sounds.

8. This name is given to large bats with wingspans reaching 5 feet, or 1.5 meters. They live in tropical areas and are also called fruit bats because of their diet. Some flying fox species use echolocation, while others have large eyes and excellent night vision.

## Chapter 3 – Worksheet 2

1. Eddies

2. If a bird flies too fast, its wings must continually fight the drag that results from the swirling air. In contrast, if the flight is too slow, air turbulence tends to "stick" to the feathers and interferes with the forward motion.

3. The maximum stroke frequency of the wing is multiplied by the vertical distance traveled by the wing tip during the flapping stroke. This number is then divided by the bird's forward speed.

4. .2-0.4

5. Design small aircraft for the military and underwater submersibles

6. Swifts and peregrine falcons are the fastest known creatures with speeds approaching 200 miles per hour. Homing pigeons are also record-setters with speeds variously reported at 100–200 mph. Even the tiny hummingbird achieves an impressive 60 mph. On land, the cheetah manages short bursts of 70 mph. Pronghorn sheep and jackrabbits have speeds slightly less. In contrast, the fastest human runners reach 20–25 mph. Under water, the speed of sailfish has been measured at 70 mph, tuna at 48 mph, and dolphins at 30 mph. Olympic swimmers can reach nearly 5 mph for

short stretches. The maximum speed of military submarines is classified, but may exceed 40 mph (35 knots).

7. The Eurasian Kestrel is a variety of falcon. The flapping of its wing is measured at 5.61 strokes/second, with an amplitude or maximum wing displacement of 0.339 meters. Its typical speed is 18 mph (8.1 meters/second). The formula gives (5.61 strokes/sec) x (0.339 meters)/(8.1 meters/sec) = 0.235 for the Strouhal number. This low number implies that the Kestral flies with extreme energy efficiency.

8. No, instead they have large pectoral fins that enable them to take short gliding flights. In escaping predators, they can glide 164 feet (50 m) or more through the air.

## Chapter 3 – Worksheet 3

1. The wings attached to the hind limbs in a delta-wing pattern rather than the front limbs

2. The rear wing would not interfere with walking since the wing membrane was elastic and could be folded against the reptile's body.

3. The canard

4. Instead of evolutionary progress, the fossil lizard indicates the loss of a particular flight design.

5. They based their design on bird gliding rather than flapping as da Vinci had.

6. The first word means "Sharov's wing," named for researcher A.G. Sharov, who reported the Russian fossil discovery in 1971. The second word is Latin for "wonderful," or "miracle," well-chosen for this expert flyer.

7. A wind tunnel is a laboratory chamber used to study the motion of animals or vehicles through air. With the object held firmly in place, air is rapidly released through the chamber at high speed. A visible vapor such as smoke can be added to the air flow and photographed as it moves around the object. This vapor indicates streamlined motion of the object in air, or turbulent resistance to motion.

8. Orville and Wilbur Wright succeeded with the first controlled, powered flight on December 17, 1903. The initial flight lasted 12 seconds and

covered a distance of 120 feet. This event took place at Kitty Hawk, North Carolina.

## Chapter 3 – Worksheet 4

1. 200 miles per hour (322 km per hour)

2. When a train exits a tunnel at high speeds, there is a rapid expansion of air that was compressed in front of the train. This results in a loud sonic boom that rattles windows and awakens people. Japan has strict laws on sound pollution.

3. When the bird hits the water, it experiences a drastic change in pressure. This difference is somewhat similar to the air pressure change of a bullet train emerging from a tunnel into open air. Wind tunnel experiments show that the kingfisher's bill is ideally shaped for a smooth, streamlined transition from air into water.

4. Total energy consumption is reduced by 15 percent

5. The recessed headlights of some trains are modeled after the nostrils of the kingfisher.

6. Kingfishers live worldwide in woodlands and wetlands. About 90 species have been identified with great variety in size and color.

7. The kingfisher eye has an egg-shaped lens that flexes to focus in both air and water environments. Our eye lens has a similar, more limited, ability to change its focus, called accommodation.

8. When compressed air rapidly expands, a pressure wave moves outward at the speed of sound. Air molecules transmit the disturbance somewhat like a row of railroad cars bumping into each other. When the disturbance reaches our ear, the eardrum vibrates and we hear the sound. Thunder creates a similar result because air expands rapidly when heated by lightning.

## Chapter 3 – Worksheet 5

1. First, the forward fringe on the owl's wing is uneven, with a tattered appearance. Second, the feathers covering the owl's wings, body, and legs are velvety soft.

2. Special curved wing feathers

3. For stealth technology purposes; to lessen noise to nearby residents

4. Increased air traffic without an increase in noise

5. They create an unwanted drag on the aircraft's motion

6. Two large examples are the Eurasian Eagle Owl and the Great Gray Owl. Their length from head to tail reaches 28–33 inches. In contrast, two of the smallest owls are the Least Pygmy and Elf Owls, each just 3–4 inches long.

7. About 200 species of owls are known. An additional 40 extinct species have been found as fossil remains.

8. The decibel (dB) measures the loudness of sound, named for Alexander Graham Bell. The logarithmic nature of decibels allows a great range of sounds to be expressed in convenient numbers. Typical loudness values include a quiet room (20 dB), ordinary conversation (60 dB), a truck ten feet away (90 dB), and the threshold of pain (120 dB).

## Chapter 3 – Worksheet 6

1. Sleep, mate, catch insects, scoop up water

2. Six

3. The adjustment or "morphing" of their wing shape

4. Dutch and Swedish scientists

5. Small aircraft with moveable wings for surveillance

6. There are at least three leading ideas on animal flight. Each assumes the development of feathers from reptilian scales, and wings arising from forearms. The curosial and aboreal models were proposed a century ago. The former suggests that short jumps became longer and longer over time, until the animal left the ground completely. The aboreal model suggests that creatures glided down from trees, eventually conquering the air. A third model, called pouncing proavis, is more recent. The suggestion is that predators pounced on prey from tree branches. In time the pounce became a swoop, and finally turned into controlled flight. In contrast to such models, the idea of flight created by God from the beginning of creation is the credible and refreshing preference.

7. Swifts tend to build nests from sticks and mud on vertical surfaces. The locations include caves and chimneys. Swifts also construct nests under the eaves and outdoor decks of homes.

8. They may look similar but are quite distinct. Swallows are songbirds and tend to fly closer to the ground than swifts.

## Chapter 3 – Worksheet 7

1. It is a third of the bird's height

2. It should topple over

3. It only makes up 5% of its weight.

4. The outer surface is made of keratin, the common protein material found in our own fingernails and hair. The keratin coating in the toucan beak consists of overlapping hexagonal layers that are somewhat flexible. This allows for bending and twisting motions of the beak. Meanwhile, the interior of the beak contains a foam-like, criss-crossed scaffold of tiny, flexible, lightweight bones. Some internal parts of the beak remain hollow, surrounded by the lattice of supporting bones.

5. Lightweight safety helmets, protective cushion panels for cars and aircraft

6. Toucans are distributed across Central and South America. The main country locations include Argentina, Bolivia, Brazil, and Paraguay.

7. The standard evolutionary reason for the bright and bold male colors found in nature is for advantage in attracting a mate. In the creation view, the colors found everywhere in nature, whether bird feathers or sunsets, show the Creator's glorious artwork.

8. A woodpecker can drill into hard wood with 1,000 taps per minute. Several safety mechanisms are in place. Its strong bill is separated from the skull with sponge-like cartilage that serves as a shock absorber. A thick skull with spongy bones also cushions the bird's brain. Strong neck muscles keep the head aligned and prevent harmful twisting. The feet have X-shaped toes positioned both forward and backward for firm grasping. Stiff tail feathers provide additional leverage against the tree. There are surely other unknown internal mechanisms that protect the woodpecker. Toucans, woodpeckers, and all other birds are excellent examples of creative design.

## Chapter 4 – Worksheet 1

1. Engineers from Mercedes-Benz and DaimlerChrysler

2. The boxfish

3. The skin of the boxfish consists of hexagonal, bony plates that give extra strength while minimizing weight.

4. A prototype compact car

5. The hexagonal skin pattern of the boxfish

6. One variety of boxfish, called the cowfish, reaches a length of 20 inches (50 cm). Most adult boxfish are smaller, around 5 inches (13 cm) long. Small boxfish specimens, just one inch long, may be purchased from pet shops for saltwater aquariums.

7. The boxfish inhabits the Atlantic, Indian, and Pacific Oceans.

8. Boxfish are part of a larger order of fish called Tetraodontiformes. This includes 350 known groups such as boxfish, puffers, and ocean sunfish. There are more than a dozen known boxfish species, including the buffalo trunkfish and the long-horned cowfish. Additional species will surely be found.

## Chapter 4 – Worksheet 2

1. They are a broad group of sea life including starfish and sea urchins. Members of the group are invertebrates that display a radial symmetry in their overall shape.

2. Thousands of transparent microlenses, each about 0.0004 inches across.

3. Gives extra strength to the skeletal structure while providing vision in all directions

4. The brittlestar lenses are perfectly aligned to compensate and cancel this light distortion.

5. The design of the microlenses is advanced beyond any optical devices manufactured today.

6. They live in all the oceans and extend from polar regions to the tropics. Brittlestars thrive in shallow areas, and also are abundant in deeper ocean depths, a mile or more down.

7. The great variety of eye structures found today in nature is thought to have developed from a single light-sensitive cell. This original photoreceptor then somehow depressed into a cup or eyeball shape, filled with fluid, and later diverged into the many types of eyes found today. Many scientists prefer the majestic statement of Psalm 94:9, "He that formed the eye, shall He not see?"

8. Calcite is one of the most abundant minerals on earth. In addition to the lenses of extinct trilobites and living brittlestars, calcite comprises most seashells. Calcite also precipitates from water to make limestone, and forms large crystals in caves.

## Chapter 4 – Worksheet 3

1. The cuttlefish, a marine mollusk, is one of the most intelligent of all invertebrates. Cuttlefish range in size from two inches to three feet or more (5–9 cm). They live worldwide in tropical and temperate oceans. The swimming motion of cuttlefish results from waving or undulating continuous fins arranged along the sides of its body. The cuttlefish displays the fastest color-changing ability of any known animal.

2. Beneath its skin are many small elastic sacs, called Chromatophores, each sac filled with color pigments. Attached muscles expand or contract these sacs, changing the cuttlefish appearance in less than one second. The pigments include the colors brown, red, and orange.

3. Deeper under the skin of the cuttlefish are white patches made of cells called leucophores that function as mirrors. These surfaces reflect the colors of the cuttlefish's nearby environment. When the cuttlefish swims beneath green seaweed, for example, it appears to instantly turn green.

4. Rapid color-changing gel that can be applied to military clothing and equipment

5. The special ability suggests that squid may communicate detailed information to each other, even while they remain camouflaged and invisible to predators.

6. Along with the well-known chameleon is a host of other color-changing creatures. In water, octopuses and flounders alter their appearance to blend in with surroundings. Frogs, toads, crabs, and prawns also can lighten or darken their skin. The male goldfinch is bright yellow in summer and olive colored in winter. Seasonal color changes also occur for the arctic fox, ermine, and snowshoe hare. It is even suggested by some that dinosaur skin had color-changing features.

7. Cuttlefish are indeed prized for food, especially in Asian countries. Cuttlefish bones are also softened and eaten. Ongoing genetic research seeks to increase the nutritional value of cuttlefish meat.

8. Light consists of vibrating electric and magnetic waves or fields. In unpolarized light, these moving waves vibrate in all possible directions. When the waves are all aligned in the same direction or plane, the light is said to be polarized. If these waves could be seen within a beam of light, they might all be moving up and down vertically, with no horizontal wave motion.

## Chapter 4 – Worksheet 4

1. This unusual fish is able to generate and detect weak electric fields. The elephant nose fish quickly notices prey, predators, and potential mates in its vicinity by the small changes they cause in the surrounding electric field, also called the aura.

2. A weak, harmless electric field can be generated by electronics when the car is operating. A passenger disturbs this electric field, depending on body size. In a stopping emergency, when a child is present, the airbag deployment can automatically be lessened or deactivated.

3. Electric fields are useful for the robotic sensing of objects, and also for the detection of intruders in homes.

4. It produces electric signals to detect obstacles and to communicate with other knifefish. This amazing creature is also able to "jam" or distort the signals of rivals. It generates an electric pulse with a frequency that mimics that of nearby competitors. This pulse confuses the sensing ability of other knifefish, which then swim away.

5. Military submarines and airplanes use similar electronics jamming strategy devices for their defense.

6. An electric field is a concept used to describe the invisible force of attraction or repulsion acting at a distance between electric charges. Electric and magnetic fields were first suggested as a visual aid by Michael Faraday (1791–1867).

7. Electric eels have several specialized organs that become electrically charged in series, somewhat like the plates of a car battery. The eel's prey may be stunned with 500 volts and one ampere of current. Intense electric fields accompany the eel's electric discharge.

8. The narwhal lives in cold Arctic waters and grows to a length of 26 feet (8 m). This creature has a long tusk that extends about half its body length. A spiral groove covers the tusk surface. The function of this tusk is not known, and may be an antenna for echolocation.

## Chapter 4 – Worksheet 5

1. A smooth, streamlined path through the water using minimal energy

2. First is a skin coating of mucus that cuts down on drag and frictional energy losses. A second major fish advantage for propulsion is the fin and tail structures that are much more efficient for thrust than the common screw propeller or paddlewheel.

3. Polyethylene oxide

4. The serrated or scalloped edges increase lift and diminishes drag when compared with smooth edges on flippers.

5. Olympic swimsuits typically have a fabric surface that mimics the skin of sharks. This fabric has tiny v-shaped ridges, called dermal denticles that reduce water turbulence and drag.

6. Some fast animal swimmers include the sailfish (68 mph), Mako shark (60 mph), blue fin tuna (43 mph), and dolphins (37 mph). Top human swimmers move through water at about 5 mph.

7. Humpback whales, especially, leap entirely out of the water, twist, and then land with a loud splash. Suggestions for this activity include communication, defense, skin care, predatory

behavior, and simply looking around. Many whale watchers believe that whales breach for the entertainment of spectators.

8. The current view is that certain small land mammals began spending more time in the sea, and their descendants gradually became whales. The mammal's legs changed into flippers, the tail broadened into flukes, and in the buoyant water world the body became enormous. Fossil evidence for these changes is lacking.

## Chapter 4 – Worksheet 6

1. By refracting or bending incoming light rays through the eye's cornea and lens

2. The lobster eye works by the reflection of light from tiny, flat mirror-like surfaces. Its eye consists of thousands of rectangular tubes arranged on the outer eye surface. Light enters these small openings and reflects inward off the shiny inside surfaces. Precise alignment of the mirrors directs the separate light rays so that they focus together on the retina receptors.

3. A new generation of x-ray space telescopes

4. X-ray radiation passes directly through ordinary mirrors, unless it hits at a small glancing angle, whereupon it reflects.

5. An outgoing, parallel beam of x-rays

6. X-rays are a high-energy form of light. The sun's spectrum of light includes a small component of x-rays. They have a wavelength hundreds of times smaller than visible light and readily penetrate matter.

7. X-rays are emitted by matter that experiences extreme heat or motion. Thousands of x-ray sources are detected in space. Many of them are at locations where matter is being pulled inward by the gravity of nearby massive stars.

8. Yes, freshwater crayfish, also called crawfish or crawdads, have a reflective optics system closely similar to lobsters.

## Chapter 4 – Worksheet 7

1. It is strong and durable. It functions in turbulent salt water, and like all other materials from nature, it is biodegradable.

2. The element iron. Such metal atoms have not previously been found in similar biological functions.

3. Polyphenolic protein

4. Further understanding of the mussel's bio-adhesive glue

5. A chemical understanding of the mussel glue

6. Zebra mussels, especially, are a serious problem in the Great Lakes and other inland waters. Their larvae are carried worldwide in the ballast tanks of ships. When released, the mussels multiply rapidly and may clog the intake pipes of waterworks and power-generating plants. They also foul pumps, navigation buoys, and boat hulls. Their growth upsets food chains and threatens fish populations. There is even the potential of zebra mussels invading plumbing systems and plugging interior sprinkler systems.

7. Such materials readily decompose, usually by bacterial action. Examples include almost all natural materials and some commercial products such as detergents and paper.

8. Superglue has the generic chemical name cyanoacrylate, $C_5H_5NO_2$. It was discovered accidentally in the 1940s by researcher Harry Coover while at Eastman Kodak. The strong, instant glue was popularized on television in 1959 when one drop placed between metal plates was shown to support a person's weight.

## Chapter 4 – Worksheet 8

1. Yes

2. Yes

3. The arm becomes articulated into short, straight sections that are quasi-jointed.

4. The octopus arm may illustrate the optimum solution for point-to-point movement of robotic arms.

5. A flexible robotic arm could wrap around objects to move or retrieve them.

6. Yes, octopi can regrow lost arms. Incidentally, these creatures have a short lifetime, usually only six months to five years.

7. The Giant Pacific Octopus has arms that may reach 13 feet (4 m) long. This creature may weigh well over 100 pounds. When newly hatched, however, an octopus may be as small as a grain of rice.

8. Canadian-built robotic arms have been a part of the U.S. space shuttle fleet for decades. The arm, or crane, is 50 feet long and moves successfully with great precision. The International Space Station has a newer generation Canadian robotic arm. This jointed device can move about the station's exterior like an inchworm. That is, the two ends take turns attaching and unfastening from outside brackets on the space station.

## Chapter 4 – Worksheet 9

1. A layered, internal structure

2. The "bricks" are tiny crystals of calcium carbonate, $CaCO_3$, held in place by the "mortar," a network of proteins.

3. About a million

4. The fabrication of biological hard tissue and artificial bone

5. Improved body armor and the manufacture of extremely strong composite components for aircraft and automobiles

6. The name is centuries old. The word *mother* was used in early English to describe hardened layers, and the word *pearl* may derive from their spherical shape.

7. Traditional implants are made of metal alloys including stainless steel, titanium, and cobalt. New composite materials, suggested by seashells, have many advantages over metals.

8. Mother-of-pearl has long been made into buttons by punching disks from seashells. The material is also used in jewelry and is inlaid in furniture and musical instruments.

## Chapter 4 – Worksheet 10

1. Colorful snail-like marine animals with fringe-like projections instead of shells. They range from an inch to two feet in size (1–60 cm).

2. Eject protective, inky chemicals into the water.

3. An unpleasant mixture of hydrogen peroxide,

ammonia, several acids, and purple dye

4. A salve for wounds

5. In community water supplies

6. The defining limits of sea slugs are not clear, but more than 1,000 species are known. New species are found regularly around the world.

7. The term is applied to any microscopic living thing, either plant or animal, and especially describes bacteria.

8. There are many names, including lettuce, butterfly, angel, and sea cucumber. Some of these colorful creatures are kept in saltwater aquariums.

## Chapter 4 – Worksheet 11

1. A sea sponge; 3,280 feet (1,000 m) deep in the western Pacific Ocean

2. First, the sponge fibers grow at the temperature of ocean water, whereas commercial fibers are produced in high-temperature, glass-melting furnaces. As a second advantage, the sponge fibers are coated with an organic sheath that toughens them.

3. They can be twisted and even tied in a knot without breaking.

4. Its fragile nature

5. Behavior whereby distinct organisms benefit from mutual cooperation

6. The common material is glass or silica, $SiO_2$, the composition of sand. Clear plastic strands are also shaped into fiber optics.

7. Yes, well-preserved sponge fossils are found in rocks around the world. There is evidence that many fossils, including sponges, are a result of the Genesis Flood event.

8. There are endless examples of symbiosis in nature. On the microscopic level, nitrogen-fixing bacteria called rhizobia live in the root nodules of legumes. In the sea, clown fish dwell among the tentacles of sea anemones for mutual protection from predators.

## Chapter 4 – Worksheet 12

1. Cold, darkness, and extreme water pressure at great depths; in addition, communication and location of one's position become difficult when the vessel is submerged.

2. That of whales

3. Streamlined, efficient movement through water with minimal noise or water turbulence

4. The whale's thrusting tail

5. Sonar (sound navigation and ranging)

6. Blue whales are by far the largest living animals. They grow to a length of 110 feet (33 m) and weigh more than 200 tons. This is 15 times heavier than the largest elephants. There may have been land dinosaurs that approached the weight of blue whales, but there also may have been larger whales in the past.

7. Whales regularly dive, or "sound," to depths of hundreds of feet or meters. Sperm whales have been monitored to a depth of 6,562 feet (2,000 m), and they may go far deeper. The pressure at this depth is 116 times greater than standard air pressure.

8. Whales make sounds that are variously described as clicks, whistles, cries, howls, and songs. The underwater vibrations allow whales to stay in contact when miles apart. In fact, sensitive instruments can detect whale sounds over a distance of 2,000 miles. The meaning of these whale sounds is poorly understood by researchers.

## Chapter 5 – Worksheet 1

1. No

2. Have a solid bony structure. The ankylosaurus had plates and protrusions consisting of multiple layers of collagen fibers.

3. The fibers crisscrossed each other at right angles, an arrangement similar to that of modern fiberglass.

4. Great strength and protection from predators

5. Construction of strong, protective barriers along highways.

6. Fossil dinosaur eggs are either round or oblong, and range from an inch to a foot in size. Nests and petrified eggs are found in many places, including Argentina, Canada, China, India, Mongolia, and western U.S. states.

7. The number is uncertain because many dinosaur finds are only partial fossils. Authorities estimate about 700 known species, and perhaps an equivalent number still unknown.

8. Modern fiberglass was invented by Russell Games Slayter of Owens-Corning Company in 1938. Its initial use was for insulation, still a major application today.

## Chapter 5 – Worksheet 2

1. To re-grow certain body parts

2. A hundred times slower

3. The internal chemical signals that trigger the annual regeneration of antlers

4. Stem cells

5. The repair of human tissue and organs and new treatments for arthritis, osteoporosis, and immune disorders

6. The moose has impressive antlers that may reach six feet (1.8 m) from tip to tip. However, the record antler size belongs to the Irish elk, or giant deer. Now extinct, these majestic animals once lived in Europe. Some fossilized antlers measure 12 feet (3.6 m) across, twice the size of the largest moose antlers.

7. As the animal ages, the antlers grow larger, but there is no direct connection between age and number of "points." A deer's first rack may have two to six points, and the increasing number levels off with age. Antlers are shed each mating season.

8. Stem cells occur in all living things, both embryos and adults. They are able to develop into a large number of specialized cells and replicate (duplicate) themselves. Stem cells may become muscle, nerves, organs, or skin tissue. The differentiation of stem cells is controlled by their internal genes.

## Chapter 5 – Worksheet 3

1. Whenever the boat deck became wet, it was slippery and dangerous.

2. Wave-like grooves on the pads

3. He cut grooves in a zigzag "herringbone" pattern.

4. The grooves allowed the shoe sole to deform slightly and to grasp the ground surface. When the surface was wet, the grooves channeled water outward from under the shoe.

5. The first non-skid deck shoes, called Sperry Top-Siders

6. The crisscross pattern is found in brickwork, hardwood flooring, paving stones, tire tread, weaving, embroidery, and not the least, in the bone arrangement of herring.

7. Many tire treads feature a V-shaped herringbone pattern that channels away surface water while maintaining good traction.

8. Go to sperrytopsider.com.

## Chapter 5 – Worksheet 4

1. The ability to run upside-down across ceilings while hunting for insects

2. A microscope shows that their toes are equipped with a carpet of scales holding a half-million tiny brush-like projections called setae. Each of these seta then branch further into finer hairs.

3. van der Waals bonds and capillary attraction

4. By incorporating water-repelling keratin within its hair follicles

5. Surgery to bond tissue together, automobile tires with greatly increased traction, glue-free tape, climbing gear, building materials

6. J.D. van der Waals (1837–1923) was a Dutch physicist. The force named for him is a weak electrical attraction between molecules. The capillary force is a similar weak molecular attraction that draws water up a straw, or into a paper towel.

7. Two researchers at 3M Company, Spencer Silver and Arthur Fry, made the weak adhesive in the laboratory. Arthur later realized that this material could hold temporary bookmarks in his church choir hymnal. In 1977, 3M began marketing the popular post-it notes.

8. Many of them have microscopic hairs on their legs that function similar to geckos.

## Chapter 5 – Worksheet 5

1. A condition where blood may pool around the heart and thorax

2. The return of the gravity force causes blood to pool in the lower extremities, limiting circulation to the astronaut's brain.

3. A series of circulation valves in the neck prevents major blood pressure changes in the giraffe's head. Also, the giraffe's legs have especially tight skin and strong muscles. These features prevent blood from pooling in the long legs of the giraffe.

4. The giraffe

5. When experiencing acceleration, pressure is temporarily increased around a person's legs to prevent blood buildup. In effect, the blood is pushed upward toward the brain to prevent fainting.

6. There are a number of space hazards besides fluid shift, including muscle weakening and bone density loss. Astronauts perform daily exercises to counter these effects and maintain health. These include treadmills and bungee-type stretching. Efforts to control fluid shift include the wearing of constrictive cuffs.

7. Male giraffes grow somewhat taller than females, reaching a height of 16–20 feet (5–6 m). The neck and shoulder height averages 12 feet (3.7 m). The giraffe has seven neck vertebrate, the same as people.

8. To provide sufficient blood pressure, the heart of an adult giraffe weighs about 22 pounds (10 kg). This is 30–40 times heavier than a human heart.

## Chapter 5 – Worksheet 6

1. The thickness of an adult person's wrist

2. One side of this bone has a pea-sized hole, called the foramen, where blood vessels enter the interior of the bone.

3. The foramen opening is surrounded by flexible material that directs stresses toward stronger regions of the leg bone.

4. Under extreme stress, the openings are not the source of breakage or failure.

5. Additional strength while decreasing weight

6. Yes, there are natural openings or foramen in some of our bones; for example, our upper arm humerus. Beside horses, other animals also have foramen bone openings for the entrance of nerves and blood vessels.

7. Race horses achieve speeds approaching 40 miles per hour.

8. When a person stands on one foot, the stress in the tibia leg bone can reach the extremely high value of 1,450 pounds/in$^2$ ($10^7$ newtons/meter$^2$). For its protection from fracture, the bone slightly contracts when under such stress.

## Chapter 5 – Worksheet 7

1. No

2. External eye fluid

3. Birds of prey, including eagles, falcons, and hawks

4. Colored masks or screens that are more transparent and safer than the old-style dark masks that obstructed vision

5. Improved vision in bright sunlight, haze, or fog

6. Penguins inhabit many parts of the Southern Hemisphere. This includes Antarctica and the southern tips of continents. One penguin species is found in the Galapagos Islands, on the equator.

7. The height of emperor penguins reaches 3.5 feet (1.1 m). In contrast, the adult fairy penguin is only 1.5 feet tall (0.5 m).

8. Orange-tinted sunglasses reduce or eliminate blue light, a major component of glare. Ultraviolet light is also at the blue end of the spectrum, and "blue-blocking" sunglasses minimize eye damage from UV.

## Chapter 5 – Worksheet 8

1. The undersides of slippery, wet leaves

2. While the gecko has many dry hair follicles on its feet, frog feet have microscopic bumps raised above a thin mucus film.

3. Dry friction

4. Mucus sticks to the leaves by "wet adhesion."

5. Cleats and mucus

6. Tree frogs are common across mid-North

America. They also range into Asia and North Africa.

7. These creatures become very noisy on spring evenings, especially when rain is approaching. A falling barometer precedes rain, and tree frogs are somehow sensitive to the changing air pressure. The decibel level of a group of tree frogs can reach an impressive 70 decibels, rivaling the noise of a lawn mower or chainsaw.

8. There are more than 5,000 frog species. Frog populations have declined in recent decades and the reason is uncertain. Suggestions include climate change, disease, habitat loss, pollutants, and predators.

## Chapter 6 – Worksheet 1

1. No

2. A combination of carbon dioxide and body odorants

3. "Masking" odors that some people give off

4. At least eleven

5. Effective, natural insect repellants resulting in relief to people, pets, and livestock

6. It is only the females that bite, in order to get a blood meal. Protein obtained from the blood helps their egg production. Both male and female mosquitoes are also nectar feeders.

7. There are a large number of chemical repellants, including citronella, permethin, picaridin, DDT, and DEET. Also somewhat effective are natural oils from catnip, eucalyptus, and soy beans.

8. Mosquitoes are vector agents. That is, they carry harmful viruses and parasites from person to person without getting sick themselves. Especially dangerous are yellow fever, dengue fever, and malaria. Millions die from malaria each year, many of them African children.

## Chapter 6 – Worksheet 2

1. Embedded in the cells of all living organisms

2. Two intertwined chains of connected atomic molecular structures

3. A blueprint or recipe for the composition and internal activity of plants, animals, and people.

4. As much information as one trillion compact discs.

5. Computer memory

6. The letters are shorthand for deoxyribonucleic acid. This is a twisted or helical chain structure present within all living cells. Researchers James Watson and Francis Crick are credited with the discovery of DNA's helical form in 1953.

7. The tightly wound helical structure is about 25 angstroms wide and millions of times longer. If uncoiled, a DNA molecule would stretch to about six feet. It would be invisible since it would consist of a string of individual atoms.

8. This equation expresses the equivalency of energy (E) and mass or matter (m), related by the speed of light (c). One gram of matter, if completely converted to energy, would produce the equivalent of 20,000 tons of explosive. Providentially, the energy release process is difficult.

## Chapter 6 – Worksheet 3

1. As thin as tissue paper

2. The slightest changes in air pressure

3. His mother and wife were deaf.

4. The bones of the inner ear amplified the slight vibrations of the eardrum. The signal then passed into the liquid filled cochlea, or inner ear, where electrical signals were directed onward to the brain.

5. The microphone and the loudspeaker

6. Bell shared in 30 patents covering a vast range of inventions. They include the phonograph, nickel-iron battery, audiometer, metal detector, and vehicles for air and water travel.

7. These are the smallest bones in the human body. Based on shape, they are called the hammer, the anvil, and the stirrup. Their Latin names are the *malleus, incus*, and *stapes*.

8. On this day, all telephones served by the Bell Telephone system went silent for one minute as a tribute to the great inventor. In his later years, Bell did not like interruptions and refused to have a telephone placed in his study.

## Chapter 6 – Worksheet 4

1. Unique personal identification

2. More than 35

3. At least 266

4. No

5. Iris scanning

6. The iris acts like the aperture or diaphragm of a camera, controlling the amount of incoming light. The iris consists of a colored fibrovascular film of cells. Depending on the amount of light available, muscles cause the iris to either dilate or constrict. This expansion and contraction controls the light entering the interior of the eye through the pupil. In darkness, the iris pulls back and the pupil opens wide.

7. This number, one followed by 78 zeroes, is entirely beyond useful comparisons. The known stars roughly match an estimate of all the sand grains on the seashores of earth, $10^{22}$, or ten billion trillion. This number is 56 zeros smaller than $10^{78}$. The number of atoms in all the visible stars of the universe is estimated at $10^{70}$. This immense number is still 100 billion times smaller than $10^{78}$.

8. Iris technology is used at several airports and international border crossings. Some U.S. public schools and businesses are also experimenting with the identification method.

## Chapter 6 – Worksheet 5

1. Through a clotting mechanism

2. A protein called fibrin

3. The fibrin forms a sticky web embedded with fragments of body cells.

4. The fibers were found to stretch more than four times their initial length, and then spring back to original size.

5. None

6. Hemophilia is a genetic disorder in which certain blood-clotting factors, or chemicals, are absent. As a result, the body cannot make fibrin to seal wounds, and bleeding persists for a long period of time.

7. Coumadin is a natural anticoagulant found in many plants. The artificially formed variety is called warfarin. It inhibits the formation of vitamin K clotting factors. This and similar medicines are called vitamin K antagonists, and are effective in thinning the blood and preventing strokes.

8. The mechanism of blood clotting requires precise reactions of many interrelated chemicals. If any one of these biochemical steps is missing, the mechanism may fail. An entire graduate course could be built on our limited understanding of the blood-clotting process. Many scientists conclude that blood clotting is far too complex, and essential, to evolve by mere chance. Instead, it shows divine planning of the internal workings of living creatures.

## Chapter 6 – Worksheet 6

1. No

2. They help grip slippery object. They greatly improve our sense of touch.

3. 100 times more sensitive

4. They allow helpful vibrations to stimulate our nerves, no matter which way the finger moves across an object.

5. Improved artificial hands

6. Yes, fingerprints are unique, even for identical twins. In such cases there are close similarities, but also measureable differences.

7. From the spacing of fingertip ridges and typical motions of the hand, the resulting vibration passed on to sensory nerves centers around 250 cycles/second.

8. There is great variety of fingertip detail in the animal world. The most widespread monkeys, called macaques, have straight-line ridges parallel to their fingers, rather than our familiar swirls. This is one of many differences between people and animals.

## Chapter 6 – Worksheet 7

1. The human femur or thighbone

2. It is located off-center from the bone.

3. Anatomist Hermann von Meyer

4. Swiss engineer Karl Cullman

5. French engineer Gustave (Gustavo) Eiffel

6. The femur, from the Latin word for thigh, is our longest and strongest bone. The average length for adults is 17 inches (43 cm).

7. The tower weighs about 10,000 tons. It is an open and relatively lightweight structure. A large cylinder of air, the size of the tower at its base and the same height, would weigh more than the tower itself.

8. About seven million people visit the Eiffel Tower in Paris each year, the most-visited paid monument in the world.

## Chapter 6 – Worksheet 8

1. They tend to be stiff and awkward to control. In space, they tend to push objects away rather than retrieve them.

2. They have extreme agility and gracefulness in motion and control.

3. Multiple arm muscles, lubricated joints

4. Sections of the wire being heated or cooled

5. No

6. The number varies between 650 and 850, depending on how muscle bundles are distinguished and counted. The arm contains dozens of distinct muscles.

7. Some common metals with high thermal expansions are aluminum, magnesium, selenium, tin, and zinc. Lengths of these metals increase by 10–20 millionths of the original length, with each degree of temperature increase.

8. Consider the "clean and jerk" event in which the barbell is first lifted to a front squat, then jerked overhead in a standing position. The record lift is 586.4 pounds (266 kg). The muscles of the human body display very impressive strength.

## Chapter 6 – Worksheet 9

1. Care for one's own needs and generally to look after oneself

2. Dutch researchers

3. An abundance of simple proteins called histatins

that fight infection, and compounds that cause epithelium skin cells to close over a wound

4. They heal more quickly.

5. They are easier to manufacture and purify.

6. Just the opposite. Saliva contains several compounds that are antibacterial in nature, and they hasten healing.

7. This common practice is a form of self-medication called *zoopharmacognosy*. Similar to that of people, animal saliva has healing qualities. Animals are "programmed" by their Creator to cleanse and treat wounds as best they can.

8. Scientists cultured skin cells in a dish, then scratched them and treated some with saliva. The "wounds" of the treated cells healed much more quickly than the untreated cells.

## Chapter 6 – Worksheet 10

1. The epidermis

2. Nutrients

3. It covers the injured cells, stems the loss of blood, and prevents infection.

4. A catalyst material is embedded in the outer coating of the polymer surface. The inner region contains a network of small channels filled with a liquid chemical resin. When a crack or fracture reaches the underlying channels, the liquid resin oozes outward and meets the catalyst, and hardening takes place.

5. Until the internal liquid agent is consumed

6. Our skin averages 14–21 square feet (1.3–2 m2) of surface and comprises 15 percent of body weight. Just one square inch of skin typically has 20 blood vessels, 650 sweat glands, and more than 1,000 nerve endings.

7. The word *plastic* comes from the Greek verb meaning "to mold or shape." Plastic surgeons usually do not use synthetic polymer or plastic. Instead, they reshape a person's bone, cartilage, muscles, fat, or skin. The purpose may be cosmetic or the repair of injury.

8. There is much current research on the health needs of burn victims. Sheets of artificial skin are available to cover exposed areas and allow

the lower, dermal skin layer to repair. At a later time, the synthetic layer is removed, allowing the outer, epidermal skin layer to grow. The sheets are variously made of animal collagen, silicon, or nylon. There is also some success with cultured skin, taken from the patient and grown externally, then later reapplied.

## Chapter 6 – Worksheet 11

1. Tooth enamel

2. About as thick as a dime

3. It acts as a shock absorber to prevent cracking of the tooth.

4. They eventually crack, dislodge, or wear down.

5. A coating of true enamel armor

6. The tooth coating is chiefly the mineral hydroxyapatite. It is also called calcium phosphate with formula $Ca_{10}(PO_4)_6 \cdot 2(OH)$. This chemical is also one component of our bones.

7. This is a popular story that is not true. Washington lost his teeth at an early age due to gum disease. He had several dentures prepared over the years, some of which are on display at the Smithsonian Museum. One set is made of ivory from the tusk of a hippopotamus.

8. Many centuries ago, false teeth were made of metals such as gold or lead, and also from human or animal teeth. In colonial times, bone and ivory were popular denture materials. Modern dentures consist of plastic, porcelain, or high-quality acrylic resin. The latter artificial teeth are molded and tinted to match each patient.

## Chapter 6 – Worksheet 12

1. A paste-like material called vernix caseosa

2. Infection

3. Heat loss

4. 80 percent

5. Vitamin E

6. *Vernix* is Latin for "varnish," describing the coating on the newborn. The second word is Latin for "cheesy," also describing the appearance of the protective material.

7. No other land mammals, including apes, produce vernix-type material in the fetal stage. This is a problem for evolutionary linkages between animals and people. Some sea mammals do produce an equivalent birth material that is valuable to babies in the watery world.

8. Ultraviolet light, or UV, is also called black light. It has a wavelength shorter than visible light, and causes sunburn on unprotected skin.

## Chapter 7 – Worksheet 1

1. Like an accordion

2. Origami

3. Other trees, wings of beetles and butterflies

4. A single pull extends the map to full size, and a downward push collapses the map once again.

5. They must be folded for the initial rocket journey into space.

6. Orgami is the ancient Asian art of constructing intricate objects and animals with folds and creases in paper. The word has Japanese roots that mean "paper folding."

7. When a butterfly emerges from the pupa, its wings are crinkled and wet. The initial, intricate folded nature of the wings has not yet been analyzed. The butterfly pumps blood into the wing veins to inflate them. As the wings dry, they stiffen and become useful for flight and also oxygen exchange.

8. One example is a folded bamboo house used for emergency shelters. It was designed by Tang & Yang Architects of Savannah, Georgia.

## Chapter 7 – Worksheet 2

1. Fully 60 percent

2. More than 3,000

3. Ethnobotany

4. Less than one percent

5. Zoopharmacognosy

6. The chemical called "aspirin" forms naturally in the bark of the weeping willow tree. The use of willow bark to reduce fever is ancient, and is described in fifth century B.C. writings from

Hippocrates. Native American Indians also discovered the pain-relieving nature of aspirin and made medicinal tea from willow tree bark. The drug was first synthesized by German chemist Hermann Kolbe in 1859.

7. The name is short for acetylsalicylic acid, or salicylic acid. The chemical formula is $C_9H_8O_4$. This white, crystalline drug is useful for relieving a number of ailments.

8. Revelation 22:2 describes future trees in the New Jerusalem. Their leaves are useful for "the healing of the nations." Ezekiel 47:12 further describes these medicinal leaves.

## Chapter 7 – Worksheet 3

1. Velcro®

2. Tiny flexible nylon hooks and loops

3. Zippers, buttons, and snaps

4. Micrometer-size electromechanical velcro surfaces; They offer an adhesion ability that can be instantly turned on or off as needed.

5. Feathers

6. Beyond clothing, some uses of Velcro include blood pressure cuffs, car bumpers where the hooks and loops are made of stainless steel, and ready-to-assemble furniture.

7. On flexible surfaces, Velcro can be readily pulled loose. On rigid surfaces, where all the hooks and loops must separate at once, the strength is far greater. Depending on the surface area, the holding force may be hundreds of pounds.

8. The location is an industrial region of Orange County, California, where hundreds of companies make sports apparel. The name comes from the instant success of startup companies with new ideas.

## Chapter 7 – Worksheet 4

1. Broad or horse beans

2. Food

3. Control the flow of fluids by either contracting or expanding

4. Calcium atoms

5. Micro forceps for grasping objects and piston for movement in micro motors.

6. The word is Italian for bean. Other names for this legume include bell, broad, field, tic, and vicia faba.

7. Some countries cultivate fava beans for food. The plant also has a root system that prevents erosion and absorbs nitrogen from the soil.

8. In ancient Greece and Rome, such beans were used in voting. A white bean counted as a yes and a black bean meant no.

## Chapter 7 – Worksheet 5

1. Weeds

2. Commercial herbicides

3. Allelopathy

4. The roots produce an amino acid that is toxic to nearby weeds.

5. Natural sorghum

6. The herbicide glyphosate is sold under such brand names as Roundup and Touchdown Total. Annual worldwide use is estimated at 15–20 million pounds in agriculture, and about one-third this amount additionally in landscaping.

7. Allelopathic vegetation includes spotted knapweed, garlic mustard, nutsedge, black walnut, eucalyptus leaf litter, and several desert shrubs.

8. More than 300 distinct species of fescue are catalogued. They vary in height from just inches to over six feet (several cm to 1.8 m).

## Chapter 7 – Worksheet 6

1. The ability of their large leaves to quickly shed water and dust.

2. Lotus leaves are covered with countless tiny bumps 0.005–0.01 millimeters high, and also a waxy film.

3. Water droplets, because of their surface tension or stickiness, touch the leaf surface only at the high points. Because of this limited contact area, the water drops quickly roll off the leaf. Along the way, they pick up soil particles like tiny snowballs and pull them off the leaf.

4. Superhydrophobic

5. A self-cleaning spray that repels water, dust, and grime.

6. The beauty of the flower has long been associated with divinity. The plant was venerated in early Asia, Egypt, and Persia. The water lily remains the national flower of India and Vietnam. Along with its beauty, all parts of the plant are also edible.

7. The dried disk resembles the sprinkler spout of a watering can. These seed pods are often used for tabletop decoration when dried.

8. This is the tendency of liquid molecules to adhere together. Two liquids with extremely high surface tension are the element mercury and water. Both readily form beads on a smooth surface. This property of water is very important. As two examples, the surface tension keeps our joints lubricated, and also allows water to move to the tops of trees through tiny capillary tubes within the trunk.

## Chapter 7 – Worksheet 7

1. Osage Orange bush

2. Michael Kelly, 1868

3. Thorn Wire Hedge Company

4. 100,000 tons each year

5. One million miles

6. The bush produces a round, bumpy fruit four to five inches in diameter. It is not edible for people or animals. However, its oils are found to repel pests, including cockroaches, mosquitoes, and spiders.

7. Sites include the Devil's Rope Museum in McLean, Texas, Ellwood House and Museum in DeKalb, Illinois, and the Barbed Wire Museum in LaCrosse, Kansas. The facilities display over 2,000 varieties of barbed wire.

8. This is a registered trademark name. The barbed wire or "tape" is a mesh of sharp metal strips designed to prevent passage by people. It is an effective visual deterrent used where high security is needed.

## Chapter 7 – Worksheet 8

1. High-tech clothes that automatically adjust to changing weather conditions

2. When body temperature increases, tiny openings appear in the fabric to increase air circulation. As temperatures fall, the openings reseal.

3. Pine cones

4. England, for military use

5. Julian Vincent

6. Yes, the cones of some jack pines and California Torrey pines may remain dormant for 10–20 years. The eventual, intense heat from a forest fire causes them to open and disperse their seeds.

7. It is female pine cones that open when warm and dry, the best conditions for germinating their seeds by wind-blown pollen from male pine cones.

8. Future "healthy clothes" may have built-in sensors to monitor the wearer's heart rate, breathing, and temperature.

## Chapter 7 – Worksheet 9

1. He noticed natives in Haiti playing games with a flexible ball.

2. It was made by hardening a gummy fluid tapped from certain trees.

3. Making shoes and rain-proofing fabric

4. Around 1770 scientist Joseph Priestly discovered that the tree gum also erased pencil marks by rubbing it on the paper.

5. Sulphur, vulcanization

6. The white sap-like gum, called latex, occurs in capillary tubes that spiral up the tree within the bark. These vessels are cut and drained without harming the tree, somewhat like the tapping of maple trees.

7. In 1774, Priestley isolated and identified oxygen gas. Oxygen makes up 21 percent of our atmosphere, next after nitrogen, which comprises 79 percent.

8. Rubber consists of long polymer chains, which are molecules with repeated units of carbon and hydrogen atoms. Sulfur atoms provide strong

cross-link connections between the chains, tying them together. The result is rubber, which is harder, more durable, and resistant to chemical breakdown.

## Chapter 7 – Worksheet 10

1. Several hundred

2. It has the ability to bloom in early spring inside a snow bank, and may produce a miniature ice cave. Its stalk can reach a temperature that is 63 degrees F or 35 degrees C warmer than the cold surrounding air.

3. The emission of strong odors that attract pollinating insects

4. A thermostat for heating and air conditioning

5. Japanese scientists

6. The odor of an undisturbed plant is mild. If a leaf is damaged, however, a definite skunk-like odor results. This smell attracts insects for pollination, and also discourages eating by larger animals.

7. There are many flowers that do not "smell like a rose." The Arum family of flowers, with about 25 species, is also known as a corpse flower. The champion may be titan arum, which grows in Indonesia. Its enormous blossom may reach several feet across. The smell, something like rotting flesh, has been known to make people pass out. Certain insects are drawn to this odor and serve as pollinators.

8. Two distinct metals are fused together. These metals, copper and aluminum, for example, have different coefficients of thermal expansion. This means that they expand differently with increasing temperature. This causes the metal strip to bend or curl as temperature changes. The resulting movement allows electrical contact, which turns a circuit either on or off.

## Chapter 7 – Worksheet 11

1. Photosynthesis

2. Converts carbon dioxide and water into new plant material while releasing oxygen

3. First, they harvest light-sensitive proteins from spinach leaves. A layer of this protein material then is deposited on a glass slide with silver electrode wires attached. When light shines on the surface, the spinach proteins generate a weak electrical current.

4. Pure silicon is difficult to produce, expensive, and fragile. In addition, living plants are able to repair or replace degraded proteins.

5. The efficient collection and use of light energy

6. The following equation describes the conversion of light energy to chemical energy by living organisms:

$6CO_2$ (gas) + $6H_2O$ (liquid) + light energy >

$C_6H_{12}O_6$ (glucose) + $6O_2$ (gas)

7. Light photons, or particles, give their energy to outer electrons of carbon atoms. The electrons that are knocked loose and the resulting "holes" left behind can then drift through the silicon crystal, resulting in an electric current.

8. Every hour, solar energy hitting the earth supplies more energy than the entire world population uses in a year. Much of this energy is reflected back into space or absorbed by the oceans. Still, there is great potential for meeting earth's energy needs by harnessing solar energy. Current challenges include the low efficiency of present technology. Today, only about 0.1 percent of the world's electric energy needs are met by solar collectors.

## Chapter 7 – Worksheet 12

1. Snap instability

2. A slight disturbance of the cilia by an insect

3. The leaf does not close unless two adjacent cilia are moved, or one cilia is touched twice.

4. A change or wrinkle of the polymer surface could result from chemicals indicating food spoilage.

5. The enclosed polymer containers could transport drugs in the bloodstream, snapping open when they reach their target area.

6. The plants are not tropical and can survive mild winters. Many are found growing wild in North and South Carolina and Florida. They prefer the nitrogen-poor soil found in bogs. As a houseplant, the Venus flytrap requires high humidity, as in a terrarium.

7. Pitcher and cobra plants trap prey in a liquid chemical pool held within a rolled leaf. The sundew plant attracts insects to a sticky surface, like flypaper. Bladderworts suck aquatic insects into their interior. Over 1,000 carnivorous plant species are known.

8. Flytraps can catch large beetles, grasshoppers, and small frogs or mice. However, they are no danger to larger pets!

## Chapter 7 – Worksheet 13

1. What was it called? London, 1851, the Great Exhibition

2. A botanist name Joseph Paxton

3. The structure of a tropical water lily called Victoria amazonica

4. The intricate pattern of veins on the underside of the Victoria Amazonia lily

5. 108 feet high and covered 18 acres of ground

6. The flower is named for England's Queen Victoria (1819–1901). She was British royalty during the time of the Great Exhibition in 1851. The water lily lives in the shallow tributaries of Brazil's Amazon River.

7. The building held 14,000 technology displays gathered from around the world. This period, part of the Victorian era, was a high point of the industrial revolution. Featured at the exhibition were steam power, electricity, and other new technologies. Popular features in the Crystal Palace included elegant restrooms, called "retiring rooms."

8. It is called a symmetric radial dendrite pattern. From the center of the lily pad, smaller veins branch off from larger veins.

## Chapter 7 – Worksheet 14

1. The ability to plant itself in soil

2. Awns

3. Small hair-like barbs along the fibers

4. To give motion to micro machines, to convert solar energy into energy of motion to be turned into electricity

5. Moisture changes the spiral shape stem, causing

it to slowly rotate and drill the seed into the soil, similar to a turning screw.

6. One major difference is that wild wheat readily sheds its ripened grain. This blowing seed then plants itself and grows elsewhere. With domestic or cultivated wheat, the grain tightly adheres to the dead stalk. This retention allows easy harvesting.

7. The host of adjectives for wheat include winter, miracle, soft (high in starch), hard (high in protein), and common wheat, often used for bread flour.

8. This plant is abundant in the western United States and Canada. It prefers dry, sandy soil.

## Chapter 8 – Worksheet 1

1. 1985

2. A soccer ball

3. Architect R. Buckminster Fuller

4. Lubricants, electrical insulators, and surface coatings

5. Carbon nanotube

6. There are two interconnected shapes, pentagons (five sides) and hexagons (six sides). Both buckyballs and soccer balls have surfaces covered with 12 pentagons and 20 hexagons.

7. Roughly one-quarter million (250,000) buckyballs could fit side-by-side across the width of a period.

8. Such domes, often made largely of glass, have great strength because the supports are under compressional forces. The buckyball is similarly strong because of the many chemical covalent bonds between carbon atoms.

## Chapter 8 – Worksheet 2

1. The natural purification of water that occurs in streams and rivers

2. At least 15 million

3. Tiny metal particles, the size of the finest dust, can break down poisons without producing harmful by-products.

4. Iron

5. More than nine million

6. Water pollution is a worldwide problem. It is especially serious in Africa, Asia, and East Europe.

7. Yes, there are microorganisms that decompose oil. The bacteria use enzymes to break down the oil molecules, and then consume them for energy. This happens continually across the earth at sites of natural oil seepages and man-made spills.

8. Such a particle would contain a thousand or more iron atoms.

## Chapter 8 – Worksheet 3

1. An internal structure of tiny layered silica spheres

2. The combination of refraction, reflection, and diffraction of light between the layers

3. Photonic

4. Lasers, fiber optics, holography, waveguides, and lithography

5. The direction and behavior of light beams

6. Leading countries for opal output are Australia, Ethiopia, Mexico, and the United States. About 97 percent of new opal comes from Australia.

7. Lithography is a printing process using chemicals to form an image. Today it includes the production of integrated electronic circuits.

8. Instead of moving electrons, light beams are used. Research continues to replace electrical transistors, switches, and gates with optical analogs.

## Chapter 8 – Worksheet 4

1. They are compact, dense stars with a very rapid spinning motion.

2. Because the entire star is collapsed inward to form a sphere of neutrons

3. More than an entire train, including all its cars and contents

4. Astronomer Jocelyn Bell

5. They offer precise time standards.

6. Such stars are incredibly dense. Their mass or weight is comparable to the sun, yet they are 150,000 times smaller. Just one teaspoon of neutron "stardust" would weigh a billion tons.

7. The nearest known neutron star is in the direction of the southern constellation Corona Australis, 200 light years away.

8. Such a visit would be perilous. Near the surface we would be vaporized by the star's intense heat and radiation. In addition, with a gravity force of 100 billion times that of earth, any nearby object would be flattened out to a single layer of atoms.

## Chapter 8 – Worksheet 5

1. Should include three of the following: galaxies, hurricanes, tornadoes, rising smoke, seashells, flowers, and water whirlpools

2. Transport fluid from place to place

3. They outperform conventional blades in the quantity of fluid moved, and far less energy is used.

4. As a key component of fans, pumps, turbines, propellers, and small, ultra-efficient cooling fans

5. Small, ultra-efficient cooling fans

6. A number of precise, elegant equations describe the gentle curves of spirals. Archimedes' spiral has the polar equation $r = a\Theta$. A logarithmic spiral is given by $r = ae^{b\Theta}$. In these formulas r is radius distance, $\Theta$ is angle; a and b are constants.

7. Both items have rotating blades that move air or liquids. An aircraft or boat propeller thrusts air or water in a desired direction, and the vehicle recoils in the opposite direction. An impeller is usually placed in a pipeline to move a confined fluid.

8. This honor goes to spiral galaxies, such as our own Milky Way. Such galaxies are about 100,000 light years in diameter, or 600 thousand trillion miles ($6 \times 10^{17}$ miles), and contain 100 billion stars each.

## Quiz 1 – Chapters 1–2

1. Biomimicry

2. Using molecular motors

3. Energy-producing microorganisms

4. Protecting animals like dogs and cattle from cholera infection, or biofilms added to paint to prevent barnacles from attaching to the surface of boats

5. These are diatoms that researchers hope to encourage growth into new and useful shapes.

6. The lights cause a faint current of electricity to pass thru adjacent layers and by putting multiple layers in series, the plant-based protein generates a useful electrical current.

7. Locusts

8. Countless interactions between nearby ants

9. Southeast Asia

10. Hydrogen peroxide ($H_2O_2$)

11. The butterfly effect

12. Four distinct wings

13. Cold light

14. A smaller "fly-sized" hearing aid

15. Light first enters through a micro lens, which caps the outer end of the column. The light then moves through the hollow column until it meets photoreceptors at the internal end.

16. Faint vibrations

17. If the robot is overturned, the mechanical legs can be pivoted 180 degrees downward and the upside-down machine can continue walking forward.

18. Upon reaching a certain size, the water droplets overcome electrostatic attraction forces and roll down the beetle's tilted back to its mouth.

19. Because of possible improvements to everything from bulletproof vests to suspension cables for bridges

20. The self-cooling systems these termites build into their termite mounds.

21. Oregon chain

22. It was made from cotton and linen rags and of limited quantity

### Bonus Questions

1. Along with the axe, crosscut saws date back to Roman times. These saws cut horizontally through the tree trunk, across the grain. Such saws improved over time with new metal alloys and tooth design. They are still much used around the world, often with a woodsman on each end of the saw.

2. The striders move by "digging" their feet into the water surface and generating vortices or tiny swirls. Pushing against the resulting "mini wall" of water, they recoil forward rapidly with speeds measured at five feet per second (1.5 meter/sec).

## Quiz 2 – Chapters 3–4

1. Parallel navigation

2. Design small aircraft for the military and underwater submersibles

3. Instead of evolutionary progress, the fossil lizard indicates the loss of a particular flight design.

4. When a train exits a tunnel at high speeds, there is a rapid expansion of air that was compressed in front of the train. This results in a loud sonic boom that rattles windows and awakens people. Japan has strict laws on sound pollution.

5. Special curved wing feathers

6. The adjustment or "morphing" of their wing shape

7. The outer surface is made of keratin, the common protein material found in our own fingernails and hair. The keratin coating in the toucan beak consists of overlapping hexagonal layers that are somewhat flexible. This allows for bending and twisting motions of the beak. Meanwhile, the interior of the beak contains a foam-like, criss-crossed scaffold of tiny, flexible, lightweight bones. Some internal parts of the beak remain hollow, surrounded by the lattice of supporting bones.

8. The skin of the boxfish consists of hexagonal, bony plates that give extra strength while minimizing weight.

9. The design of the microlenses is advanced beyond any optical devices manufactured today.

10. Rapid color-changing gel that can be applied to military clothing and equipment

11. A weak, harmless electric field can be generated by electronics when the car is operating. A passenger disturbs this electric field, depending on body size. In a stopping emergency, when a child is present, the airbag deployment can automatically be lessened or deactivated.

12. A smooth, streamlined path through the water using minimal energy

13. A new generation of x-ray space telescopes

14. It is strong and durable. It functions in turbulent salt water, and like all other materials from nature, it is biodegradable.

15. The octopus arm may illustrate the optimum solution for point-to-point movement of robotic arms.

16. The fabrication of biological hard tissue and artificial bone

17. A salve for wounds

18. Its fragile nature

19. Cold, darkness, and extreme water pressure at great depths; in addition, communication and location of one's position become difficult when the vessel is submerged.

20. Streamlined, efficient movement through water with minimal noise or water turbulence

## Bonus Questions

1. Swifts tend to build nests from sticks and mud on vertical surfaces. The locations include caves and chimneys. Swifts also construct nests under the eaves and outdoor decks of homes.

2. A woodpecker can drill into hard wood with 1,000 taps per minute. Several safety mechanisms are in place. Its strong bill is separated from the skull with sponge-like cartilage that serves as a shock absorber. A thick skull with spongy bones also cushions the bird's brain. Strong neck muscles keep the head aligned and prevent harmful twisting. The feet have X-shaped toes positioned both forward and backward for firm grasping. Stiff tail feathers provide additional leverage against the tree. There are surely other unknown internal mechanisms that protect the woodpecker. Toucans, woodpeckers, and all other birds are excellent examples of creative design.

## Quiz 3 – Chapters 5–6

1. No

2. The internal chemical signals that trigger the annual regeneration of antlers

3. The first non-skid deck shoes, called Sperry Top-Siders

4. The ability to run upside down across ceilings while hunting for insects

5. A series of circulation valves in the neck prevents major blood pressure changes in the giraffe's head. Also, the giraffe's legs have especially tight skin and strong muscles. These features prevent blood from pooling in the long legs of the giraffe.

6. Under extreme stress, the openings are not the source of breakage or failure.

7. Colored masks or screens that are more transparent and safer than the old-style dark masks that obstructed vision

8. Cleats and mucus

9. A combination of carbon dioxide and body odorants

10. Computer memory

11. The bones of the inner ear amplified the slight vibrations of the eardrum. The signal then passed into the liquid-filled cochlea, or inner ear, where electrical signals were directed onward to the brain.

12. Iris scanning

13. Through a clotting mechanism

14. The fibers were found to stretch more than four times their initial length, and then spring back to original size.

15. It is located off-center from the bone.

16. Multiple arm muscles, lubricated joints

17. They heal more quickly.

18. A catalyst material is embedded in the outer coating of the polymer surface. The inner region contains a network of small channels filled with a liquid chemical resin. When a crack or fracture reaches the underlying channels, the liquid resin oozes outward and meets the catalyst, and hardening takes place.

19. Tooth enamel

20. A paste-like material called vernix caseosa

## Bonus Questions

1. Orange-tinted sunglasses reduce or eliminate blue light, a major component of glare. Ultraviolet light is also at the blue end of the spectrum, and "blue-blocking" sunglasses minimize eye damage from UV.

2. These creatures become very noisy on spring evenings, especially when rain is approaching. A falling barometer precedes rain, and tree frogs are somehow sensitive to the changing air pressure. The decibel level of a group of tree frogs can reach an impressive 70 decibels, rivaling the noise of a lawn mower or chainsaw.

## Quiz 4 – Chapters 7–8

1. Origami

2. Fully 60 percent

3. Velcro®

4. Control the flow of fluids by either contracting or expanding

5. Allelopathy

6. A self-cleaning spray that repels water, dust, and grime.

7. Thorn Wire Hedge Company

8. Pine cones

9. He noticed natives in Haiti playing games with a flexible ball.

10. A thermostat for heating and air conditioning

11. First, they harvest light-sensitive proteins from spinach leaves. A layer of this protein material then is deposited on a glass slide with silver electrode wires attached. When light shines on the surface, the spinach proteins generate a weak electrical current.

12. A change or wrinkle of the polymer surface could result from chemicals indicating food spoilage

13. The intricate pattern of veins on the underside of the Victoria Amazonia lily

14. To give motion to micro machines, to convert solar energy into energy of motion to be turned into electricity

15. Lubricants, electrical insulators, and surface coatings

16. Tiny metal particles, the size of the finest dust, can break down poisons without producing harmful by-products.

17. Lasers, fiber optics, holography, waveguides, and lithography

18. They offer precise time standards.

19. One of the following: galaxies, hurricanes, tornadoes, rising smoke, seashells, flowers, or water whirlpools

20. As a key component of fans, pumps, turbines, propellers, and small, ultra-efficient cooling fans

## Bonus Questions

1. Pitcher and cobra plants trap prey in a liquid chemical pool held within a rolled leaf. The sundew plant attracts insects to a sticky surface, like flypaper. Bladderworts suck aquatic insects into their interior. Over 1,000 carnivorous plant species are known.

2. The building held 14,000 technology displays gathered from around the world. This period, part of the Victorian era, was a high point of the industrial revolution. Featured at the exhibition were steam power, electricity, and other new technologies. Popular features in the Crystal Palace included elegant restrooms, called "retiring rooms."

# *Discovery of Design* ➥ Test Answer Key

1. Energy-producing microorganisms

2. Protecting animals like dogs and cattle from cholera infection, or biofilms added to paint to prevent barnacles from attaching to the surface of boats

3. Hydrogen peroxide ($H_2O_2$)

4. If the robot is overturned, the mechanical legs can be pivoted 180 degrees downward and the upside down machine can continue walking forward.

5. The self-cooling systems these termites build into their termite mounds.

6. Instead of evolutionary progress, the fossil lizard indicates the loss of a particular flight design.

7. When a train exits a tunnel at high speeds, there is a rapid expansion of air that was compressed in front of the train. This results in a loud sonic boom that rattles windows and awakens people. Japan has strict laws on sound pollution.

8. The design of the microlenses is advanced beyond any optical devices manufactured today.

9. Rapid color-changing gel that can be applied to military clothing and equipment

10. The fabrication of biological hard tissue and artificial bone

11. No

12. A series of circulation valves in the neck prevents major blood pressure changes in the giraffe's head. Also, the giraffe's legs have especially tight skin and strong muscles. These features prevent blood from pooling in the long legs of the giraffe.

13. Colored masks or screens that are more transparent and safer than the old-style dark masks that obstructed vision

14. Cleats and mucus

15. It is located off-center from the bone.

16. Fully 60 percent

17. Velcro®

18. A self-cleaning spray that repels water, dust, and grime

19. A thermostat for heating and air conditioning

20. The intricate pattern of veins on the underside of the Victoria Amazonia lily

## Bonus Questions

1. The mechanism of blood clotting requires precise reactions of many interrelated chemicals. If any one of these biochemical steps is missing, the mechanism may fail. An entire graduate course could be built on our limited understanding of the blood-clotting process. Many scientists conclude that blood clotting is far too complex, and essential, to evolve by mere chance. Instead, it shows divine planning of the internal workings of living creatures.

2. To avoid predators, the color of this beetle matches its frequent habitat, bright white fungi. How the fungi itself produces this color is yet another marvel that is not well understood. The beetle's reflective surface also provides cooling for its body.

## Chapter One

1. Number 4, the edge of your hand

2. The hand in this orientation simulates a wedge shape, which slices through the water. The other shapes have a larger frontal area, which cause more drag.

3. All shapes with rounded ends

4. Dolphins, squid, birds

## Chapter Two

1. The corrugations and the popsicle sticks ran parallel with each other and provided no rigidity in the other direction.

2. Gluing down the second set of popsicle sticks 90 degrees to the corrugations provided the increase in strength.

3. There would still be additional strength added, as long as the second set of popsicle sticks do not run parallel with the cardboard corrugations.

## Chapter Three

1. Able to break thread and paper, unable to break the remaining materials

2. Thread should have been the easiest

3. You were probably unable to break the fishing line.

4. metal, wood, plastic

## Chapter Four

1. Yes, after drying, the paper's shape changed and became wrinkled, resulting in the paper contracting.

2. Yes, the sponge did also shrink in size, but did not significantly change its shape as compared to the paper.

3. No, they did not. The sponge took more time to dry because of the larger size and the fact that it absorbed more water than the piece of paper.

## Chapter Five

1. It would make no difference.

2. No, the only way is to physically glue it down.

## Chapter Six

1. The only way is to make the air intake end stiffer to prevent it from moving all around. One method is to add tape around it a number of times to increase the thickness.

2. Less air in the balloon means less pressure, which will result in the balloon moving more slowly.

3. The farther away you stand, the more difficult it will be to hit the target. The closer you are, the better chance you have of directing the balloon through your friend's arms.

## Chapter Seven

1. Violet, indigo, blue, green, yellow, orange, red

2. The rainbow will shift and/or disappear.

## Chapter Eight

1. 360 degrees

2. A peak and trough

3. Since the peak of one wave will occur at the trough of the other wave, the net result is that they would cancel each other out in their entirety and result in a flat line.

## Chapter Nine

1. Will be dependent on your camera, but your eyes will have a larger field of view than your camera. Some cameras have what is called a panoramic view setting which will provide you with a field of view far wider.

## Chapter Ten

1. 27

2. Will vary from individual to individual

3. $4 \times 4 \times 4 \times 4 = 1024$

4. Thousands every day, which are variants of existing viruses

## Chapter Eleven

1. It should be a little more difficult to perform three tasks as compared to one.

2. Will be based on individual

3. You should be able to perform all tasks simultaneously; just be careful and take your time.

4. For a whole brain we would need 42 x 10 = 420 semi-trailers

## Chapter Twelve

1. Between the range of 450 to 500 nm

2. Green; a smaller number represents a smaller wavelength

3. Sound waves

## Chapter Thirteen

1. Hydroquinone, hydrogen peroxide, and oxidative enzymes

2. Benzoquinone

3. Fear from predators initiates its defense mechanism.

4. 2

5. 10 times the length of the beetle. Example: if the beetle is 2" long, then the range would be 10 x 2 = 20".

6. 500

7. 100 degrees Celsius

## Chapter Fourteen

1. With the glass upright, the glass did not make a deep penetration into the modeling compound. However, with the glass upside down, only the rim of the glass came in contact with the modeling compound and produced a deeper penetration. Therefore, the amount of contact area is the only thing that changed. The lower the contact area (rim of glass) the deeper the penetration.

2. Stress = P / A = book weight / area = 10 / 5 = 2 psi

3. Rearranging the equation to solve for area, we end up with area = P / stress = 40 / 20 = 2 in².

4. The proboscis vibrates at a rate of approximately 15 Hz. The vibration helps achieve the penetration depth required yet reduces the amount of force required as compared to a straight push.

## Chapter Fifteen

1. The grains of rice would deflect higher. An increase in intensity of the sound results in a higher amplitude in the sound wave, which results in further deflection of the plastic wrap. The rice is used to help visualize the effects of the sound waves on the plastic wrap, replicating sound waves on the eardrum.

2. The plastic wrap on the bowl must be taut for this experiment to be successful. Any puncture in the plastic wrap will absorb the sound waves and not result in deflection of the plastic wrap.

3. It would not make a difference, provided the sound originates within the vicinity of the plastic wrap. This is because sound travels omnidirectional (in all directions).

4. The Ormia ochracea's ears are spaced closer and are mechanically coupled via a circular disk. The circular disk sums up the difference immediately to determine the location of the sound source. Conversely, human ears are spaced farther apart and summing up is reliant on the brain downstream.

5. 3 x 24.50 = 73.50 Hz

6. For one second there are 2 peaks and 2 troughs. Therefore for 3 seconds there would be 6 peaks and 6 troughs (= 2 peaks/troughs per second x 3 seconds).

## Chapter Sixteen

1. The frozen pea, because it is the lightest

2. The quarter, because it is the heaviest

3. The frozen pea since it is the lightest

4. Yes, the pea took the longest to fall down and the quarter was the fastest.

## Chapter Seventeen

1. Hair, fruit, dirt, leaf of a plant, cotton ball

2. No, the fingertips have more pressure receptors than the back of your hand.

3. You should — the sensitivity at the tips of your finger are the same, regardless if you use a finger or a thumb.

## Chapter Eighteen

1. You will have difficulty with any surface that is porous, such as a plaster wall and wood.

2. In order to create a tight seal around the edge of the suction cup and to remove any air, moisture will be required.

3. Surgical, dentistry, ophthalmic, orthopedic

## Chapter Nineteen

1. In our example we used five clothespins. The weight of the book was 2 lbs.

2. In our example, load per clothespin = weight of book / number of clothespins = 2 / 5 = 0.4 lbs

3. Using the same book weight = 2 lbs, the number of clothespins is now 5 + 4 = 9. The load per clothespins = 2 / 9 = 0.22 lbs. From this example there is a large reduction on the load per clothespin. The more clothespins we have, the less carrying load is required from each clothespin.

4. Metal has been used and can be used for air conditioning systems in buildings, service engineering, and automotive construction. The metal Velcro has a load-carrying capability of 7,200 lbs. per square foot.

## Chapter Twenty

1. Interior shape: plastic bag; paper bag; Exterior: tissue paper, printing paper.

2. Wasp papermaking is superior. The hexagonal shapes are not easy for man to create without extra tooling to form the shapes.

3. This will vary based on individual.

## Chapter Twenty-One

1. The light will still reflect back toward you as long as you're still aiming toward the bowl.

2. The light will still reflect back toward you, but the intensity of the light will be reduced.

3. No, it will not work. Only a curved surface would be able to reflect the light back the same way it came in.

## Chapter Twenty-Two

1. Van der Waals

2. Rubbing balloon on head or rubbing feet on a piece of carpet

## Chapter Twenty-Three & Twenty-Four

Answers will vary.

## Chapter Twenty-Five

1. The water will move slower at the cap.

2. The water will move faster at the cap.

3. They need fans.

## Chapter Twenty-Six

1. Yes. it would. The ends of the "X" were glued down at the intersection of the popsicle sticks and provided rigidity. With the plus sign, the intersections would not have the same rigidity.

2. The ceilings of homes and warehouses; bridges; cranes; antenna towers

## Chapter Twenty-Seven

1. We would feel the frictional forces between our eyelid and eye, resulting in discomfort and eventually the inability to see clearly.

2. Approximately 30

3. Rearrange the equation to solve for $\mu = F / N = 100 / 200 = 0.5$

4. $F = 0.62 \times 500 = 31$ lbs.

5. Oil in a car's engine

## Chapter Twenty-Eight

1. Around 1½ feet

## Chapter Twenty-Nine

1. Plastic, wood, paper

2. You will notice that the tunnel without the cardboard will collapse first.

## Chapter Thirty

1. You could use anything that is shiny and has faceted surfaces. Shiny faceted-surface objects would work best.

2. Yes, you would have the same results as long as there was a reflected surface (plastic report cover). It would still work, regardless of the length of the can.

3. Mirrors, foil wrap, shiny metal surfaces

## Chapter Thirty-One

1. Without sunlight there would be no photosynthesis process. No oxygen bubbles were produced in the dark.

2. Yes, the results were the same.

## Chapter Thirty-Two

1. You will never see that.

2. You will notice leaves grow out from the center in a circular direction.

3. Yes they do — that is the main structural support that the leaf branches off from.

# *Made in Heaven* —● Quiz Answer Keys

## Quiz 1 – Chapter 1–8

1. resistances
2. drag
3. orientation, toughness
4. tension
5. thickness
6. strength
7. elasticity
8. tensile
9. temperature
10. metals
11. polymers
12. ceramics
13. semiconductors
14. material
15. material
16. pinecones
17. coarse
18. nanobots
19. magnetic
20. frequency
21. light
22. frequency
23. seven
24. peak
25. 360 degrees

## Quiz 2 – Chapter 9–16

1. optics
2. reflected ray
3. refracted ray
4. reflected and refracted
5. Snell's
6. index
7. camera
8. mathematics
9. cognitive
10. thousands every day, which are variants of existing viruses
11. brain
12. small
13. neurons
14. For a whole brain we would need 42 x 10 = 420 semi-trailers.
15. sine
16. color
17. visible
18. ultraviolet

19. In the range of 450 to 500 nm

20. chemistry

21. product

22. Ten times the length of the beetle. Example: if the beetle is 2" long, then the range would be 10 x 2 = 20".

23. It is the complete cycle of a sine wave (one peak and one trough) repeated per second.

24. intensity

25. platelets

## Quiz 3 – Chapter 17–24

1. fingertips

2. mussel

3. distribute

4. adhesives

5. proteins

6. reflective

7. electromagnetism

8. metal

9. proton

10. attract

11. density

12. drag

13. surgical, dentistry, ophthalmic, orthopedic

14. Metal has been used and can be used for air conditioning systems in buildings, service engineering, and automotive construction.

15. Wasp papermaking is superior. The hexagonal shapes are not easy for man to create without extra tooling to form the shapes.

16. Van Der Waals

## Quiz 4 – Chapter 25–32

1. identical

2. weight

3. They need fans.

4. truss

5. friction

6. weight

7. number

8. rougher

9. lubricant

10. windshield wipers

11. We would feel the frictional forces between our eyelid and eye, resulting in discomfort and eventually the inability to see clearly.

12. approximately 30

13. oil in a car's engine

14. sound

15. compress

16. load

17. light

18. thermodynamics

19. energy

20. chloroplasts

21. Without sunlight there would be no photosynthesis process. No oxygen bubbles were produced in the dark.

22. plant

23. rules

24. You will notice leaves grow out from the center in a circular direction.

25. Yes they do — that is the main structural support that the leaf branches off from.

# *Made in Heaven* → Test Answer Key

1. drag
2. elasticity
3. pinecones
4. nanobots
5. seven
6. optics
7. camera
8. brain
9. chemistry
10. Ten times the length of the beetle. Example: if the beetle is 2" long, then the range would be 10 x 2 = 20".

11. fingertips
12. proteins
13. reflective
14. electromagnetism
15. drag
16. They need fans.
17. windshield wipers
18. sound
19. thermodynamics
20. You will notice leaves grow out from the center in a circular direction.

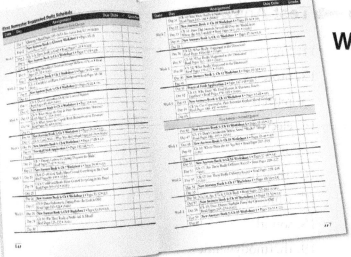